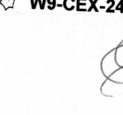

Murder In The Afternoon

Ella Jo Sadler

ZONDERVAN PUBLISHING HOUSE OF THE ZONDERVAN CORPORATION
GRAND RAPIDS, MICHIGAN 49506

This is a true story. However, some of the names and places have been disguised to protect the privacy of those involved.

MURDER IN THE AFTERNOON

© 1975 by The Zondervan Corporation

Grand Rapids, Michigan

Library of Congress Catalog Card Number: 74-25342

Printed in the United States of America

To MOTHER
who taught us a sustaining faith
and
to PATSY *and* DON
whose encouragement helped me re-create
the painful scenes
and
to MY HUSBAND
who saved my life

Contents

Murder In The Afternoon

The Setting . . .

"All that happens to us is working for our good if we love God and are fitting into his plans."

—Romans 8:28, *The Living Bible*

Under blue summer skies, the peaceful countryside around the farming community of Quaker, Missouri, is a landscape of patchwork design. Ripening grain fields, in hues ranging from maize to shades of deep gold, are interspersed with lush green pastures. The fences enclosing various sections are lined with foliage, and huge trees trace shallow branches of Cub Creek as it meanders through the area.

The lives of the inhabitants of this isolated farming region are as peaceful and ordinary as their setting. God-fearing, respectable citizens for the most part, they spend their days reaping the area's abundant harvests, enjoying neighborly gatherings and church meetings, and leading lives common to any farming community.

Little hills rise out of the meadows like bulges in a soft carpet, and occasionally a higher crest overlooks the lower expanses. The most prominent of these is a lofty peak that commands a view of the sprawling Barr valley and the secluded site of the farm and country store that have belonged to the Barr family since 1918.

The big white house with forest green shutters sits on a knoll several yards back from a straight stretch of highway. Surrounded by a wide yard filled with giant maples, it holds a warm and inviting appeal, suggesting a home and family noted for hospitality. A scarlet rambler climbs the white trellis beside the doorstep, while pink tea roses border the fence that separates the home from the wide graveled parking area surrounding the country store.

In the store, a forty-foot square building of dark stained wood with long glass windows in front and back, numerous purchases are rung up every weekday. But Saturday is the busiest as farmers halt labor in relaxed anticipation of the Sunday worship and rest. Folks shop unhurried and linger to chat with neighbors. They come in a steady stream all day until the first lull about evening mealtime.

While some people are coming to buy groceries at Barr's store, others use the day for their weekly trip to Potosi, the nearest town, county seat, and center of most business transactions, located thirty miles away. By mid-afternoon these travelers, too, have finished their most important errands, and the men are hustling their wives from the stores. "Come on, let's get home. We'll be doing chores after dark," is their usual plea. Then, homeward bound, they make their last stop of the day at the country store.

Until that fateful weekend in July of 1959, the Quaker community was a tranquil rural scene, broken only by the sound of farm machinery or the calls of the meadowlark and bobwhite. But when the first shotgun blast shattered the hush of that warm summer afternoon, the tranquillity was destroyed.

> *"All that happens to us is working for our good if we love God and are fitting into his plans."*

Murder In The Afternoon

Part 1 . . .
Ella Jo . . .

Friday was "business as usual" for the most part. The whole town of Potosi was rather quiet, but it mattered little to me as I looked through the wide windows across from my desk. I was anything but lonely, thinking, *This is it, Jo. The big year!* How incredible it seemed that I'd finally be a senior in high school. More than that, thrilling as it was, it was the next big step toward attaining my highest goal — studying music at a conservatory. And then, as always, I breathed the words and flashed a silent prayer that it might be so.

Last year had ushered me into that exciting era when I'd gained the long-awaited driver's license and my own set of keys to the family car. Now, with my seventeenth birthday just two weeks away, I felt much more mature. And getting this job in town had been the crowning touch.

Though I worked for a small business firm, I was usually busy, and between customers and typing assignments I could look out on one of Potosi's busiest streets. Today, however, it was as quiet inside as out, where the only sounds were the pinging of an auto mechanic's tools next door and an occasional horn out front. Thus, I found myself with time to daydream.

Glancing at the food market across the street, I noticed a white-aproned boy carrying grocery bags to the waiting cars. He was always smiling and joking with the people he helped. *What a happy guy!* I thought. *He really enjoys life — every minute.* It reminded me of my dad's attitude in his grocery business — always singing and smiling, always warm and gracious, displaying a true Christian spirit to those he served.

Between the food store and an electrical appliance center was the red brick and glass-paneled library where kids were always buzzing in and out. Just now there were three girls about my age coming through the door. As they walked down the sidewalk, a pretty blond hurried to join them.

I wondered, as I often did, about the difference between these town kids and my own friends in the country. Were they really more sophisticated? Mentally I compared our schools. There was keen rivalry between them in sports events, but the school in Potosi wasn't much bigger and certainly no better than our consolidated Valley High School. I supposed the contrast would be in the kids' pastimes.

Quite content living in the country, I didn't mind being teased about coming from "the sticks." I didn't even mind the fact that our rural community did not yet have telephone service. On days like this, with white cloud puffs scattering across a brilliant blue sky, I was only too happy to have the peaceful country setting to enjoy.

Just then a black coupe whizzed around the corner and parked beside the crosswalk where the girls were waiting. *Hey, that looks like Jerry's car.* I was startled to see him away from his job. But as the young driver jumped out, I saw that in looks and manner he was the very opposite of Jerry Sadler, my steady boyfriend. His hair was black, while Jerry's was blond. And he wasn't nearly as tall as Jerry.

They're worlds apart in attitude, too, I reflected, watching him strut across the street beside the girls. I thought of Jerry's quiet, reserved personality, so modest he wasn't even aware of his own popularity — kindhearted, always helping someone.

Since our first date I'd considered him very special, as did my whole family. Only one thing about our romance bothered me. I hoped Jerry understood how it was with my music. Since I was three I had played the piano, and I didn't intend to stop perfecting my skill for a long time — if ever.

"Music is my whole life, Jerry. It's just me!" I'd told him last weekend as we talked about the future. Attempting to explain my feelings, I'd ventured, "Maybe when you go back to college this year we should stop going steady for awhile — not stop dating, but just — well, you know what I mean. Don't you think it's a good idea?"

"No, I don't," he'd replied. He seemed baffled by my suggestion. And before the question could be resolved, we'd reached our destination for the evening and further discussion was impossible. I'd be seeing him tonight, but we'd be double-dating with my friend Bobbie Lou Shipp and her boyfriend Joe, so there would be no chance to talk about the matter. Bobbie Lou would be spending the weekend with me on the farm, too.

My thoughts were interrupted by a phone call, and from then on my afternoon was busy and passed quickly. When I finally looked at my watch, it was 4:45 — nearly time to clear my desk and leave.

I had to drive to my sister's house, where I lived during the week in town, and pick up my suitcase that was packed for my weekend at home with the folks.

Then, as I was about to turn off the small portable radio that I kept for background music, a pleasant voice caught my attention. It was the short break in the day's pop music programming — a minute meditation offered by a local minister. As I listened, he quoted the most sensational declaration from Scripture I'd ever heard.

"We know that in everything God works for good with those who love him, who are called according to his purpose."

"Wow!" I was hardly aware of my exclamation as the message really got through to me. I'd been a Christian all through my teens, and probably I had heard this verse many times before, but never had it or any Scripture hit me with such impact.

I was amazed at the idea. "In everything." Every single detail! My mind traveled the horizon of my life, surprised to think that God was really interested in every bit of it. That He'd care about the smallest detail — every life-shaping event. It was a new concept to me. It was great!

The words echoed in my thoughts as I finished work and left the office. Little did I realize the impact those same words would bring in the near future — or how vitally I would need that divine assurance.

Late that evening, wearing baby-doll pajamas and hair rollers, my friend Bobbie and I sprawled across my pink-quilted bedspread and talked about the double date we had just shared. The baseball game in St. Louis had been exciting and the evening fun. Now we were enjoying the coziness of lamplight and girl talk, which always seemed to center on "boy talk."

A vivacious personality with sparkling brown eyes and a keen sense of humor, Bobbie was a good friend and an enjoyable guest. Even more meaningful to our friendship was the fact that we shared a common faith in Christ, even though we attended different churches. Another thing we had in common were the large class rings with thick ribbon wadded underneath that both wore on our left hands. Late into the night we discussed our future plans and knotty problems bothering our friends. And when we finally decided to sleep, we first knelt together in prayer.

Certain I'd just closed my eyes, I couldn't believe it when I heard mom calling from downstairs. Streaks of sunlight poured through the sheer pink curtains, confirming the fact that it was morning.

"I hate to tell you this, Bobbie," I groaned, "but we have to leave here at 8:00 in order to get to Flat River in time for my lesson." I struggled out of bed and flopped down on the pink frilled stool, leaning my head against the white marble vanity top.

"You gotta be kidding!" Bobbie sat up and then fell back on the pillow. "This is pure torture."

"Right!" I finally struggled to the closet and handed Bobbie one of two pastel robes, and we proceeded to stumble downstairs, where we were greeted by mom and dad and more brilliant sunlight streaming into the kitchen from the adjoining sun porch.

Dad sat at the head of the breakfast nook thumbing a farm magazine while mom worked in front of the white range across the room.

"Tell us about the game, girls." Dad's dark eyes sparkled with interest. Beaming his usual broad smile, the tall man sat erect, towering above the table.

"Oh, dad, we're not awake yet."

"I believe it!" He grinned at mom and began asking teasing questions about "the guys" until we finally were alert enough to give him the details of the game and our trip to St. Louis.

Mother turned from the stove. As jovial as dad, she had a reputation for accomplishing more in any one day than several women together. In spite of her silver hair, she didn't look her fifty years. As she set a platter of fluffy scrambled eggs and smoked sausage on the table and returned to the oven for a tray of crusty homemade biscuits, she said, "Honey, grab a jar of my fresh jelly from the porch."

As I walked out onto the sun porch, I noticed the shelves were filled with glass jars of fruits and vegetables to be stored in the cellar. Whistling in surprise, I reached the end of the long rows.

"Wow, mom, you really picked some blackberries this week."

"Sure did. I was in the patch up on the back hill every morning at daybreak. The bushes were just loaded this year."

After offering a thankful prayer, we ate the delicious meal and continued a light conversation. Finishing his last buttered biscuit with a thick jelly spread, dad rose from the table still drinking from his coffee mug.

"I'd better get out in the field."

"Where are you baling today?" mom asked. "Still working at Grace and George's?"

"Yep. I think I can finish there today."

"Be sure to tell your sister about the homecoming dinner at Bethel Church tomorrow. She won't want to miss seeing her old friends."

Mom walked with him across the sun porch where he picked up his big straw hat from the rack and went through the door humming softly. As he passed the kitchen windows we could hear a sketch of his song, "Just o—ver in the glory land. . . ." Soon the sound of the tractor floated through the windows as he headed down the lane toward the main road and on to my aunt's farm five miles down the creek.

"Girls, better jump and get ready to go," mother reminded. "I'll do these dishes and put a roast in the oven before I open the store."

By the time we were dressed, she had the kitchen cleaned and lunch in the oven. She called upstairs as she went out the front door, "Nice day for your trip. Have a good time. And, Jo, drive carefully now. You hear?"

"Yes, mom." I was thrilled that the folks had allowed me to drive myself to Flat River, fifty miles away, for my weekly piano lesson. Of course, this consent was only granted if a friend could ride with me.

Soon Bobbie and I were on our way east over the scenic country route and then northeast on Highway 32 into the town where we went our separate ways — Bobbie to shop uptown, while I went to the piano studio.

"Meet you at 10:30 at Foulons," I said, "and we'll decide over malts what to do next. Okay?"

"Agreed."

Later, the next stop on our excursion was the record shop,

and the rest of the morning was spent browsing through the stores until we returned home to the farm for a late lunch.

Alone in the big house in the quiet, warm summer afternoon, Bobbie and I ate, washed dishes leisurely, and talked.

"How come you and Jerry don't argue at all?" she asked at one point. "I can't figure it. Does he ever get mad?"

"I guess not. I've never seen him upset, and we've been together a lot." I chuckled over the understatement. "We get along just great. Only one big problem —"

"Oh?"

"Well, I just can't get married next year — or the next!"

"Why not?" she asked, looking down dreamily at the amethyst stone in the ring she was wearing, a recent gift from Joe on her seventeenth birthday.

"I just can't think of it yet." I looked up from the sink where I'd been scrubbing the last plate intensely.

"See, my music has to come first. Like — I've been studying piano all my life, but really I've just started. Jerry tries hard to understand. He's sweet, and I like him a lot — but — I gave his ring back last weekend."

"You didn't!"

"He kept it a day." I held up my left hand with the large gold class ring, and we both broke into laughter, knowing that any kind of breakup between Jerry and me would have been futile.

As I closed the long glass cupboard door after putting the last dishes away, I suggested, "Shall we go up and listen to records or something?"

Unaware of time once we were upstairs and buried in albums and conversation, we didn't even look outside again until past mid-afternoon. Lifting one pink sheer to scan the road, I cried, "Hey! Isn't that Leo Blair's new car?"

Bobbie joined me to check out the shiny red convertible parked in front of the store.

"Let's go see. Maybe Mae's with him."

Zipping downstairs and outside, we walked toward the store. As we approached, our former classmate was drinking the last drops of soda while he rested on the porch edge, idly scuffling gravel with his shoe.

"Hi, Leo. How's everything?"

As the three of us talked in the late afternoon sun, we heard the throbbing motor of a tractor approaching from the road behind us, and soon dad rounded the front corner of the store.

"Hi, kids," he saluted with his broad grin. He parked the rig in the lane and approached us at his usual brisk pace. Extending his right hand, dad beamed, "Leo, it's sure good to see you again."

Perspiration beads stood out on his face and soaked his clothes. He swabbed his brow with a large handkerchief and lifted his straw hat to brush dark hair from his forehead. Fanning a gentle breeze with the wide brim, he sighed, "Whew! Hot day." Then, leaning comfortably against one of the wide columns that supported the porch roof, he remarked, "Some red car you have there!"

"Isn't that spiffy?" Leo slapped his knee, his expression showing obvious pleasure at dad's admiration.

Mom came out of the store, and dad smiled affectionately as he handed her a bulky white package.

"What's this?"

"Steaks!" His twinkling eyes were as dark as his coal black

hair. "Grace had her freezer full from the last beef they killed. She served George and me a platter of medium rare sirloin for lunch. Then you know sis — she insisted I bring some home." He smacked his lips with exaggerated fervor and added, "No doubt they're thawed by now."

"Ready to grill," mom agreed as she took them inside to one of the refrigerated storage units.

"Hon, I think I'll run up and shower. I'll be right back and take over here. Okay?"

"Sure. Go ahead. Don't hurry," mother called as she joined us to relax in the wicker chairs on the porch. The wide porch roof shaded us as the sun moved down behind the store, casting a sprawling shadow across the parking lot.

And all the time, unknown to us, strange and sinister shadows were lengthening toward the store.

A short while later Leo moved from his perch. "Guess I'd better get goin'. Gotta big date tonight." He opened the door and slid under the wheel of his prized possession. Then with a spurt of gravel he backed the car out of the driveway and burned the road to the bridge where he disappeared into the green overgrowth.

"And speaking of dates," I said excitedly, "can we get ourselves together in an hour or two?"

Bobbie laughed and joined me. "Maybe we can. I have to roll my hair again, though."

"Me too."

We began to stroll toward the house, discussing plans and what to wear that evening. Glancing backward as a car whizzed past on the highway, Bobbie asked casually, "Do you ever tend the store?"

"Sure. I take my turn," I replied, picking a thread from my dark blue shorts. "In fact, I was here alone last Saturday afternoon until closing time."

"Weren't you lonely way out here by yourself without even a phone?"

"Lonely? Not me!" I scoffed good-naturedly.

Bobbie scanned the surrounding fields and forest and the deserted road which seemed to vanish beyond the narrow low-clearance bridge. As we watched, a black sedan emerged from the green canopied bridge and continued down the road to stop in front of the store.

"Well, I wasn't actually alone all afternoon. Customers —" My voice trailed off as I nodded toward the parked car and waved to the plump lady and her lanky husband who were now greeting mother on the store porch.

"Diane Kearns was with me until five o'clock, too," mentioning another of our friends, "but Ralph came early for their date. His quartet had an engagement at seven o'clock, and they had a long drive — to Arcadia, I think, or somewhere that way. They both hated to leave me alone, but I didn't mind. And I didn't want them to be late."

"So you braved it fearlessly."

"Sure did. Stayed right in there. Jerry came just before closing time, and we left about six-thirty." I giggled suddenly. "You should have seen Diane and me last noon. We were supposed to cook this huge fish — bass or something — dad caught out of the pond."

"How'd it taste?"

"Not bad when we finally got it fried. But that thing wouldn't lie down in the skillet." My gestures imitated our attempts at flattening it, and we both shook with laughter. "The back with all those prickly bones was just out of control."

"See, dad and mom were going out to a barbecue, and they thought we should have something extra-special."

"I suppose you learned all about how to cook fish in ninth grade home-ec?" Bobbie's facetious question was asked without the trace of a grin.

"Are you kidding! We were too busy making stuff like tomato aspic," I drawled, and we both broke up laughing.

Just then dad crossed the wide front porch of the house and joined us by the gate, whistling cheerfully. "What's all the giggling about?" His big grin encompassed us. "Is this the build-up for the big date tonight?"

Bobbie grinned while I pretended nonchalance, finally collapsing with "aw dad" and pounding his shoulder playfully.

"Guess the fellas'll be out pretty soon?" Always at ease with us, he was as lively as any of our friends. In fact, this mood reminded me that his wit hadn't even been spared from the boys I'd dated. He was just as likely to tease them, given an opportunity. "Now don't they always come around on Saturday night?"

"You're right, they're coming." I agreed lightheartedly. "That is — Jerry's coming about six-thirty, and we're meeting Joe, Diane, and Ralph in Belgrade."

"Oh, yes, I remember. The quartet's there tonight. Mom and I might make it if I get out of the store in time," he planned with enthusiasm. "Those lads can really sing."

As dad started through the gate, another car stopped in front of the store. "Guess I'd better go relieve mother." He waved to the two women customers who'd just arrived. "Looks like the Hutchings. Hi, ladies! — Mildred, Effie."

As he moved toward the store, we heard his deep bass voice singing, "Now let us have a little talk with Jesus. Let us tell Him all about our troubles —" in rhythm with his brisk steps.

"Your dad really sings a lot, doesn't he?" Bobbie said as we turned toward the house and strolled across the yard.

"Sure does. He and mom used to sing in a gospel quartet," I said with pride. "But, of course, mom hasn't been able to sing much since her tracheostomy. You know, she breathes through a tube in — or did you know?" I caught her surprised look. "Most people don't notice because of the high collars she wears. She has all those lace jabots and stuff to hide it."

Coming from the store just then, mom overheard the last snatch of our conversation. Not the least bit sensitive about her handicap, she readily agreed when Bobbie asked to see her unusual breathing apparatus.

Bobbie was astounded. "I've never seen one — this close." She leaned closer as mother carefully uncased the stainless steel instrument for her inspection.

"See, I can't speak a word without it." Only by lipreading could we know what she said when the mechanism wasn't in position, and she joined our laughter after she'd replaced the curved set.

"Is it very — I mean it must be uncomfortable."

"Not at all," mom said easily. "After eight years it's almost part of me. Even the sterilizing is just a part of everyday routine." Her gentle blue eyes and soft features were completely reposed as she hinted at a problem. "Only time it's irritating is when a speck of dust or thread gets inside. There's nothing to filter it from my lungs. But really I'm not complaining. I'm just thankful to have it."

We walked through the front door, across the front porch, and into the cool living room. Mom disappeared into the downstairs bedroom and was back momentarily with an armful of clothes.

"Need anything pressed for tomorrow?" She gripped the hangers which held her persimmon-colored dress and dad's charcoal slacks and pin-striped sport jacket. "Or for tonight? You know, Sunday-go-to-meetin' type duds?"

"We're all set, mom. But we'll carry those fruit jars down to the cellar for you unless there's something else you want us to do."

"Yes, there's one thing. How about rolling my hair?" she called from the back porch just after we heard the opening clink of the ironing board.

"Sure. I'll get the pins and stuff now."

"Oh, Jo, don't forget Bonnie Sue's coming."

"Right, mom — four-thirty. She's always on the dot." Then I explained to Bobbie about my piano student. "You know Bonnie Sue Midgett, don't you? Freshman last year." As she nodded agreement, I asked, "Hope you won't mind waiting while I teach her half-hour lesson. Then we'll dash up and get ready. Okay?"

"Fine. Maybe I can help your mother do something."

By the time I had the wave-setting paraphernalia, mother was in the living room saying, "Just a few clips will be enough. My set didn't hold in some spots, and I want it to look good for church tomorrow."

Though she protested, I wouldn't quit until I'd done a thorough job. Neither of us had the slightest inkling that those metal wave clamps I placed in even rows across the back of her head would mean the difference between life and death.

Murder In The Afternoon

The Witnesses . . .

Among the last of those returning from Potosi were two neighbor women, Effie Hutchings and her daughter-in-law Mildred. They, too, stopped at Barr's store where they always bought groceries and marketed their hens' fresh eggs for pin money. This particular afternoon they didn't stay to talk since they'd been away all day, and with the car's trunk and back seat crammed with packages and grocery bags, they were soon driving again toward the setting sun.

Rounding the fenced corner of the second alfalfa field, they passed a narrow side road leading south between two high ridges toward a densely wooded section. Then they drove beside Cole Spring, banked between the rutted side trail and the western slope, a stream that flows to within a dozen steps of an old-fashioned tabernacle which was the community's central gathering place.

Past the quaint structure of cedar posts and crude benches the Hutchings car then entered a treacherous section where the road curved sharply between jutting rock bluff and a steep bank above the creek channel. Nearly through the passageway, Mildred squinted into the dazzling sun's rays around the west side of the cliff and was startled to see a tall figure emerge from the banked underbrush into the path of her car.

Swerving toward the rocks, she slowed the car as the young man whistled through clenched teeth. Before she'd completely stopped, she saw that the beanpole figure wasn't a neighbor lad, as she'd supposed, and that a companion following close on his heels carried a gun.

As the car lunged forward from Mildred's quick acceleration, she heard a shouted oath and in the rear view mirror saw the taller boy hurl his large gray hat into the air and then stomp it on the ground as he seemingly cursed the women for ignoring his signal.

Mildred relaxed her tight grip on the wheel. "What in the world are they up to?"

"Wow! They're some ugly customers, huh?" Effie sighed, looking over her shoulder.

"You didn't know them either? At first I thought it was one of the Moses boys fishing up the creek. But when I got a good look at them — wonder what they wanted?"

"Anything wrong with the car?"

Mildred checked the gauges. "Everything seems all right. Tires feel fine. Squirrel hunters maybe." And they dismissed all thought of the questionable characters as they went to their homes and casually entered through unlocked doors.

"Dad, you ready?" called Bonnie Sue Midgett as she ran down the garden path. "It's four o'clock."

"Be right with you, Bon," Marvin Midgett called as he slid from under the tractor on which he had been working.

While her dad picked up his tools, Bonnie Sue walked across the driveway to pet her fat pup, Shep, who was napping under the sycamore tree. Next to music, pets were her favorite entertainment. But then music was more than a pastime — it was a part of her. Now she was taking piano lessons from Jo Barr and loving it enough to be a good student.

Marvin joined his young daughter, and soon they were driving up the winding trail which led from their secluded home towards the Barr farm. Marvin whistled, then stopped to ask, "Did mom give you her grocery list?" Bonnie Sue handed it to him. "Good. I'll shop at the store and talk to Lynn while you take your lesson."

"You know, dad, when I get my license in a couple years I can take mom to the store, can't I?" Bonnie Sue said eagerly.

"Mom might drive herself by then," Marvin remarked. "All she needs is more spunk." He maneuvered the car over the rutted road between large oaks and countless saplings.

After turning the beige sedan left onto the graveled Ridge Road, he wound down a hill and made another left turn onto Church Road. They crossed the bridged Cub Creek at its narrowest section just above the forks, where Cub Creek ran into Courtois Creek. Around the bluff they slowed somewhat, then continued for a couple of miles until they passed the old tabernacle about a half-mile from the Barr farm. Then Marvin reduced his speed to a crawl as he pulled up beside a pair of youths moving slowly but deliberately up the road.

The Witnesses 35

"Hi, boys!" He didn't recognize the pair. Heads bowed, they kept their eyes fixed on the pavement as they continued stalking along the roadside.

"Goin' our way?" Though Marvin spoke to them with the friendliness common to the area, the two only grunted in reply. In their fleeting glance toward him, he was able to identify them. "Wanna ride?"

"Naw, we'll walk," the taller youth answered as he switched a shotgun to his left shoulder. In a moment he returned it to his right side and maintained his stumping pace.

Bonnie Sue waited until they were on their way again before she asked, "Who are they, dad?"

"That one on the outside, the tallest, is Hank Jones and the other's Jim Banks. Looks like they're hunting pretty far from home," Marvin mused.

"Where are they from?"

"Over near the Viburnum mines. I see them every afternoon on my way home. Hank's folks moved out from Leadwood — must've been about the first of the year — and his dad works in the mines. The Banks kid started palling around with him this spring when school was out. His family came from St. Louis about that time. Friendly chaps usually." Marvin looked in his rear view mirror, and Bonnie Sue turned in her seat in time to see their upturned faces before they again ducked their heads. The taller one's face was completely shaded under his big gray hat, while his comrade's stringy hair did a thorough job of hiding his eyes.

Marvin parked in the wide lot in front of Barrs and entered the store while Bonnie Sue went up to the house to have her lesson. As always, it seemed to last no more than a few minutes. Soon she was saying good-by, and they were on their way home again.

As they drove onto the road toward the glowing sunset,

the Midgetts met the same two boys they'd passed earlier. Marvin waved and spoke again, but they quickly lowered their gaze, as before, and trudged on.

What heartache there would be for the father and daughter when they learned of the scene soon to be enacted behind them.

Mrs. Dorothy Dalton and her two small daughters were just getting into their car when two boys strode onto the porch of the general store and flopped down on two of the wicker chairs.

"Hi, boys!" Lynn Barr said immediately. "Squirrel huntin?" His eyes sparkled with interest.

"Yeah." The muffled reply came from low in their throats, while their eyes were focused on the porch floor. Stroking the shotgun balanced across his knees, the taller boy adjusted his lopsided hat as he leaned closer to his partner. "That's not all we're gonna kill."

Mrs. Dalton heard the sly aside and looked from the gun across the bony knees and up to the thin face which was now turned to the younger boy for agreement. Thoughts of a deer killed out of season flashed through her mind. Then she looked away.

"I need some gas, too," she said to Lynn as he carried out the last of her grocery bags.

"Be with you in a minute, boys." He smiled at the youths who grunted an inaudible answer, seeming to be in no hurry. Soon Mrs. Dalton was on her way, leaving Lynn Barr alone with the two boys — leaving him alone.

Murder In The Afternoon

The Criminals . . .

When Mrs. Dalton had driven down the road, Lynn Barr walked back up the porch steps to join his young customers.

"You say you're out for some game?"

Hank Jones met his friendliness with a steady stare. Finally he stole a side glance at his partner who was flipping a string of hair from his eyes.

"Yeah," Jim Banks laughed and again erased stray hair from his vision. Now the taller youth was absently patting his shapeless gray hat.

Doggedly Lynn attempted conversation. "I got four squirrels one morning this week when I was checking the pasture fences up on the hill behind that wood lot." He nodded toward the barn, and the two glanced briefly in that direction where a patch of brilliant red was visible at the end of the leafy green lane.

Jones resumed his stare treatment and eased backward, shrugging his thin shoulders, then looked away up the road. Banks shuffled his heavy boots noisily and slung his head to rid his face of the greasy strands of hair.

Patiently awaiting a clue to their presence, Lynn poked gently at the tire repair tool mounted on the front post and adjusted its various clamps with his big hands. He smoothed back the dark hair from his ruggedly handsome face and surveyed with contentment the surrounding fields of white-faced Herefords and grain.

Humming a few bars softly, he ignored the boys awhile before he tried again. "You boys go to school in Viburnum?"

Banks looked up coolly. Still switching his stringy hair, the extra jerk of his head was hardly a discernible answer.

Jones spoke. "I'm out." He glanced at his companion and his thin chest heaved with suppressed laughter as he thought of his third-grade education. Rising from the chair, he pulled down the legs of his jeans to meet his too-short socks, then sank back down and riveted his eyes on the clean, late-model sedan parked in front of the house — the car that figured so largely in their plans.

When Lynn finally decided to go inside and leave his taciturn, jumpy visitors, Banks grabbed the door from his hand and followed. Only a step behind was Jones, walking with knees slightly bent, his carriage suggesting loose-jointed limbs.

Quivering hinges registered the impact of the door Jones let slam, and the sound echoed through the long room. The interior, colored with shades of light green from the high ceiling down to the stained woodwork and shelf edgings, was a cool relief from the mid-summer heat.

Before circling to the inside of the centered island counter, Lynn reached his long arm across a frozen food section to hang the long-handled clasping gadget in its high wall bracket. Continuing around the open end of the oblong counter structure, he walked its length to the cash register and his broad smile took in both boys as he stood waiting for them to speak.

Banks started pacing back and forth between the door, where he peered up the road, and a central spot. His glance roved the side walls lined with packaged and canned foods and household items. Finally he pretended to consider the cold cuts on display with dairy products and soda in the glass-fronted refrigeration unit. He looked longingly at the frosty bottles, and his eyes pleaded with Jones. *Could the plan wait?*

It had been such a long, hot walk after noon when, on credit, they'd liquored up at a tavern. The proprietor had even forced them to drink outside in the heat since he knew they were minors. Six beers gave them courage, but shortly afterward their old junk car stalled and they'd ditched it several miles down the road and walked all afternoon under scorching sun.

Once they'd thought of asking for water at a wayside house, but discarded the idea as too risky. Also, they'd considered winding up sooner by killing a store owner ten miles down the road across the county line. But it was too close to Viburnum and to "the shack," as Hank referred to his home. So they'd continued to their planned destination — this isolated country store and farmhouse.

Breaking the long silence, Lynn asked, "What can I do for you boys?"

"Ya make sandwiches?" Banks' question came through tight lips.

Barr turned and was nearing the cutting table as he answered genially, "Sandwiches? Sure. Be happy to fix some. What kind? Cheese? Bologna? Spiced ha—"

"Bloney!" Banks barked from his station near the front door.

Lynn reached into the cooler for the roll of lunch meat and placed it on the table as he turned on the electric meat slicer. He tore open a bread wrapper while he talked over his shoulder to the pair.

"It's good and fresh, all-beef." Then he began singing softly, "Just over in the glory land, I'll join the happy angel band —" as he cut generous portions to put on the bread. "Want'em wrapped?" he asked without looking up from his busy hands.

"Yeah," Banks answered, hoping to divert attention from Jones who was slowly raising the gun.

Jones carefully trained the shotgun on his target and with a practiced hand aimed at the grocer's head.

One shot was sufficient. The tall man dropped to the floor like a mighty oak felled with a small ax blow.

In the hush that followed the blast, Jones and Banks casually emptied the slain man's pockets of key rings and wallet. Finding few bills in his money folder, they tampered with the cash register, but to no avail. After trying to pry the cash drawer out with a knife, they tired of the futile efforts and walked out to the sedan parked near the gate to the front yard.

One after another they pushed the keys into the ignition

slot. Still with several untried, they became frustrated with that, too, and threw the handful of keys across the road into the creek. Pushing the car down the slope of the parking lot, they failed in another attempt to start it. Rolling easily at first, the sedan finally came to a standstill in front of the store.

Hank was ready to move on. "Nuts to this. Let's get the key up there." He nodded toward the farmhouse. "Those women drive."

"You mean they used to," chuckled Jim as they moved to complete their awful plan.

Murder In The Afternoon

Ella Jo . . .

Bobbie, mother, and I sat down to eat supper about 5:30 that afternoon. We offered a thankful prayer and soon were tasting the roast beef sandwiches, roasting ears, and iced tea. Suddenly I heard a loud blast.

"Boy, that kid's going to ruin his car," I looked at mother knowingly. "He's a real show-off," I explained to Bobbie. "Always turns the key and backfires his car engine on the bridge."

"I didn't hear any motor, though. Maybe it's a hunter," mom suggested.

Minutes later there was a loud whack against the door.

"What's that?" mom listened intently. "Is someone at the door?"

"I'll see." I hurried through the house and onto the screened porch. On the wide concrete step stood two tall figures staring at me out of hard eyes. In a flash I knew something was wrong. They stood motionless with a gun butted on the ground between them.

"Hello?" The faint tone of my question implied suspicion as I grasped the door handle.

"We want water," the taller one said bluntly and abruptly leveled the gun across his chest. His thin lips curled in a taut line, with a mocking smile that chilled my heart.

"Okay, I'll bring you —" I began, still clutching the latch, but was cut short by his snarl.

"Nope, you don't. We'll come in." Then, as if on cue, his companion yanked the door from me.

Quelling the urge to scream and run, I turned and slowly walked back to the kitchen with the two boys trailing close behind.

In the kitchen the last bright day streams tapered through the west windows after filtering through the leafed maple that shaded the yard. Just inside the kitchen door the boys stopped dead. Standing together, shoulders touching, they barricaded the doorway as they surveyed us.

"Mother, these boys want a drink," I said calmly as I crossed to the sink.

"Why yes, of course," mother seemingly retained every whit of composure, although she must have seen the terror in my eyes.

Before turning on the water faucet, I stood with my back to the invaders, temporarily blotting out their image. I longed to believe they really wanted just a drink of water. I twisted the handle too hard, spraying cold water in my face and up to the window above the sink. Icy shock, drenching my eyelids, lips, and flushed cheeks, marked the end of the fleeting escape from reality.

"This is a stickup," the tall one announced, his voice grating like a coiled rattler.

As I whirled from the sink, the tumbler crashed to the floor. Eyes blazing, the tall one stood with the cold steel weapon pointed into the faces of the two at the table. Their eyes reflected horror, but their cordial smiles remained frozen.

Seeming enraged at the silence, the gunman slammed his slouch hat to the floor, grinding it underfoot as he roared, "BY GOD, I MEAN IT!" He looked like a madman. His eyes darted fiery glints and his mouth opened to spew a flow of obscenity and filthy threats. As this ended, we were commanded to lie down on the floor.

How do you describe that moment of absolute horror, absolute terror — beyond comprehension? A scream caught in my throat and never sounded. My prayers were as ragged as my breathing. "Lord! Help? Please!" And I thought, *This can't be real!*

In a frightened daze Bobbie and I complied with the order. But mother, in a desperate decision to get help, slipped her hands from her lap to grip the chair seat beneath her. Then she screamed and made a lightning break for the back door as a shotgun blast ripped through her right shoulder, knocking her to the ground outside.

From the depths of his throat the shorter one growled, "Make sure!" While the gunman strode across the porch toward mother, the other one paced the floor scant inches from our heads, clumping between the glistening white cookstove and the breakfast nook.

In my dazed numbness I realized that Bobbie had begun screaming, calling for help, but I was powerless even to move. On the porch the killer raised his gun once more, and the blast plunged me into a world of darkness.

Ella Jo 51

Murder In The Afternoon

The Criminals . . .

Turning from the shot that had emptied his gun, Hank Jones stroked the gunstock fondly, then inverted the firearm as an answer to his partner's questioning look. Their plan had made no allowance for a fourth party or for an attempted escape. Now Banks made furtive, questioning gestures toward the two figures on the floor. Immediately Jones gripped the barrel end with both hands and began violently beating the air. Banks grinned, recognizing the alternate solution.

The girl lying near the table leg appeared to be sleeping, but the one beside the stove was screaming at the top of her lungs. One forceful blow into her right temple silenced her. Then they began on the sleeper, ruthlessly hammering her skull.

Finally they turned to finish the first girl. After a few more crashing blows on her head, the hardwood gunstock broke. Along with the chopping of bones and splintering wood, there was a harsh grating as the gun grazed the white porcelain of the oven door.

"That's one way." Jones stood up, flexing his bony shoulders and arms.

"Let's get away from here!" Banks snapped. He led, then, in the finishing touches with several savage thrusts of his heavy boots directed against the bodies of the silent girls.

"Guess they're out of it." He turned on his heel and walked into the dining room.

"Whoops. Forgot my hat," Jones yowled as he side-stepped the bloody pool and crossed to the doorway. "Gotta have my old topper." He snatched the flattened item and shook it gingerly before slapping it on his head.

Then he spied the gun by the table leg where it had landed after the final blow. "Better drop this somewhere," he said and carried it to the front door where he dumped it just inside the threshold. He was forced to wait for Banks who had discovered two purses on the coffee table in front of the sofa.

"What have we here?" The ransacker's voice was hopeful, but his face turned sour when he found no cash. Leaving the keys, wallets, cosmetics, and personal effects strewn over the polished table top, the two traipsed out of the cool, hushed house as though they'd come for a visit and found no one home.

At the store they hurriedly tried a wiring experiment under the car hood, but were soon interrupted when a truck drove into the parking lot beside them.

The driver backed the long flat-bed truck around to the side storage room where the feed was kept. Both cab doors opened, and a man stepped down along with a tall boy and two toddlers.

"Store's closed," Jones growled.

Dumbfounded, the older two looked at each other. Then without a word they hustled the lively youngsters back to the high seat and drove away.

"Lost cause," Jones finally spluttered, cursing the car with every try at the ignition.

"Time to beat it, I guess," his partner said as their last chance disappeared.

Stumping away, their feet gritted against the pebbly surface underfoot. They clambered over the fence and loped down the long alfalfa patch and over another fence. After crossing a second field, they stopped for a breather beside an oak tree.

Covering another short distance, they saw their reflection in the sparkling fresh Cole Spring. From a squatting position Banks splashed water in his face and then flung a shiny stone against the pulpit in the nearby open-air tabernacle.

"Better shed these." He indicated their blood-spattered shirts.

Jones walked through the stream, unbuttoning his shirt and letting it slide down his back into the spring. Banks followed suit, and without a backward glance they moved to the pavilion.

Leaving wet footprints across the dusty floor, they walked out from under the old landmark and reduced their gait to a saunter on their carefree way home, confident of the success of their escape from their unsuccessful plan.

Hearing an approaching vehicle, they made no attempt to hide. As the dilapidated supply wagon approached at a crawling pace, the driver leaned across the seat to speak and get a closer look.

The two grunted back, seeing the stranger as no threat to their getaway. Their victims wouldn't be found for hours. And even then, they wouldn't be talking.

Murder In The Afternoon

Valle . . .

Going down in the final shot-gun blast, Valle Barr had fully expected to awaken in heaven. Now some awareness was stirring within her. Face down in the red grass, she flinched in a futile effort to refocus her thoughts. She groaned, but only a choking sob came out. *What now? I thought heaven? Oh, this isn't — where?*

Fragrance of clover was an earthly tie reaching her senses. Sheer grit returned before full consciousness, and she spent a timeless agony of blind groping. Shoving her toes into the grass, she braced herself on one elbow as every muscle tensed to pull her body up from the ground.

On her knees, finally, she strained through the haze before her eyes to identify the pink dots swimming in midair. Then came recognition of the pink phlox growing beside a terraced grassy knoll. Closely following this came the realization of where she was and why. *How long have I been lying here?* she wondered, and prayed for strength to stand.

Desperately trying to steady her spinning world, she renewed her purpose and after a grim struggle was on her feet. The first step was an eternity. Swaying with her crazy world, she ventured a few steps. In near blindness she was about to topple, but she drew a long ragged breath and turned with determination toward the front yard. Foremost in her mind was the reechoing pulsation, *Get help... Got to make it... Go on... Go on....*

Tears and blood bathed her face. But tortured more than her battered body was her broken heart as she reeled on the front doorstep and then clung to the doorframe for a time before she was able to work the screen door open with her toe.

Only momentarily had she considered trying to reach the western sun porch where she knew Lynn kept a hunting rifle in a catch-all closet. She had rejected the possibility, knowing that she couldn't shoot and would certainly not be convincing enough to scare anyone. Now she wondered how she would even make it inside the house to get her car key as she moved slowly across the front porch.

Through her dim vision she saw the broken gun inside the living room door and eased past it, wondering. Did it mean the attackers had gone? Had her husband seen them? She dared not consider why Lynn hadn't come to investigate the shots. Dazed and almost blind, she walked on through the dining room and into the kitchen where the girls lay in the widening red pool.

They were so still, and she couldn't tell them apart. She feared they were dead, but knew if she leaned closer to check that she'd never get back to her feet.

The scene and her grief were unbearable. She blinked at her own blood-soaked dress and apron and knew she was sinking fast. But there might still be a chance. *They might be alive*. Throbbing afresh, the drive to get help made her turn her back on the two girls.

Her car key hanging on the wall plaque inside the dining room was within reach but seemed unobtainable. Her right arm hung limply from her torn shoulder, and raising her left hand only reminded her of the mangled thumb. Trembling, she grasped the key between the index and third fingers on her left hand and tried to ease it from the hanger. *Oh, if I drop it — never can pick up*. At last she had it. She stumbled through memorized space toward the front door. Her only thought was the reverberating pleas, *Lord, help me. Get help — get help — help!*

In the living room she gripped the doorjamb and shuffled her feet to avoid tripping over the gun. Grateful for the fresh air in her lungs, her thought now was to find the car and drive it somehow.

When she touched the front gate with her outstretched hand, it was with a surge of gratitude that her walk was nearly finished. She stood only a second clinging to the gate before her fingers suddenly lost their grip. She didn't even feel the hard rock surface where she fell.

Murder In The Afternoon

The Neighbors . . .

Ellis Gilliam, on his way home from his selling route, drove at his usual snail's pace. The back compartment of his vending rig was crammed with various household products and cosmetics. At his crawling pace it was easy to draw up beside the two slouching figures in the road ahead of him. Leaning across the seat to speak to them warmly, he got only sullen grunts in reply from the two teen-age boys, so he drove on.

When he passed the Barr farm, Ellis turned his head to look at the house and yard. As he did so, he caught a glimpse of movement at the front gate — *as if someone had fallen!* Then he spotted the prone figure. *Something red on the ground?* He stopped abruptly, then pressed down on the gas pedal to hasten his old van over for a closer look. By the time he was out on the ground, another car was approaching. Although this one was going much faster, the driver, Melvin Taylor, did not fail to notice the whistled hail or the man struggling to lift someone. He drove to the fence and leaped from his car.

"Why it's Valle Barr. What's happened?" The husky man saw Ellis's thin shoulders heaving in an effort to lift the still form. Quickly he slipped an arm under her shoulders.

"Dead?" He felt for her pulse. "Let's get to the hospital." His words tumbled out as he opened the back door of his new car and eased the unconscious woman onto the seat.

The two men climbed into the front, and Melvin drove at high speed, barely slowing enough for the sharp curves at each end of the narrow bridge, heading for the nearest hospital at Bonne Terre, fifty miles away.

He braked sharply at the first farmhouse, where he spotted his brother Ray and another neighbor, San Gilliam. Leaning out the window, he yelled, "Take guns, men. Valle Barr's been shot!"

Farther on, Ellis noticed a car waiting at an intersection. "Isn't that Donnie Compton?"

Melvin recognized the teen-ager's car, too, and he held down the horn as he pulled up beside it.

"What's up?" the boy questioned through the open window. Then he spotted the bloody form in the back seat.

"Valle Barr's been shot. Go see if anyone else —. We'll stop in Belgrade and send for an ambulance from Bismarck — just in case."

Melvin drove on, leaving Donnie and his companion to return to the tragic scene.

Donnie Compton left generous strips of rubber on the highway as he took off toward the

Barr farm. He'd never admit the tingling up and down his spine or the wave of nausea he'd felt at the sight of the blood-covered woman. Beside him, his cousin Harry, an older man, rode in silence. This wasn't surprising, since Harry was no talker.

A jumble of thoughts and questions tumbled through Donnie's mind. *What had happened? No telling what the others were like!* He shuddered, pushing back a shock of dark hair with his broad palm. *How could this possibly happen to the Barr family? They were real Christians.*

He rated the Barrs as "pillars of the church," mainly because of their life style and long record of Christian witness. Actually, he'd rarely seen the inside of a church. The most he knew about worship was what he'd observed through his car window overlooking a service at the open-air tabernacle. But he could recognize the "saintly type," as he'd labeled the Barrs.

What was the explanation of such violence in their lives? *What had happened?* Unanswered, these questions hung suspended in his troubled mind, repeated endlessly during the three-mile ride.

Suicide? *Never!* He knew Valle Barr well enough to answer that one. Murder? *Surely not — if Lynn were around.* Besides, murder didn't happen out here in Quaker. Maybe in St. Louis, but not here.

Donnie's thoughts centered on the youngest Barr — Jo, his former classmate. They had gone to school together from first grade on until he'd dropped out, and they'd always been good friends. He enjoyed Jo's keen sense of humor, but he also admired her firm principles, even though it meant he had to watch his language when he was around her.

Several times she'd tried to introduce him to her "best friend" — Jesus — but he'd just laughed it off. She had swell parents too. He recalled the many times they had gathered the neighborhood kids for a wiener roast or party.

Quaking from shock more than trepidation, Donnie and Harry arrived at the farm and hurried up to the front of the house. Harry went in first. Following close behind him, Donnie leaned down for a closer look at the shattered gun that lay by the front door.

"Here's the weapon, Harry. What a mess!" He straightened and found that his cousin had gone through the quiet rooms. Then, hearing Harry's deep groans, Donnie went on into the kitchen where he found him bending over the still forms of two girls lying in a bright red pool. Their hair was thick with blood and their features were so distorted that Donnie couldn't tell who they were. He cursed under his breath from the frustration and emotion welling up inside him.

"What kind of creature could do this?" Donnie muttered. As he whispered her name, the one he thought was Jo stirred slightly and then was still again. The other girl never moved, and Donnie could detect no breathing or pulse.

"Wonder who this other girl could be?" Harry's voice was choked.

"It must be Diane Kearns. She and Jo are such good friends, and I saw her here last Saturday."

Donnie looked around the kitchen helplessly, feeling a misery and sorrow unknown before in his life. He glanced across the table where the evening meal was practically untouched. A tomato slice drooped over a sandwich corner, and a row of bites had made a narrow path rimming an ear of corn. A sticky brown trail from an overturned tea glass had dripped onto the floor.

"There are Jo's glasses," he said, moving to the farthest corner and reaching under the table. As he picked them up, the slender russet frames with a tiny gold strip running across the top edge reminded him of the brunette's smiling eyes, now concealed by bruised eyelids in a swollen, bloody mask. He shook red drops from the glasses and laid them gently on the windowsill.

Both men gazed longingly up the lonely road toward the bridge, wishing for the wailing sound of the ambulance, but hearing only their own pounding hearts. The thirty-mile trip from Bismarck added to the return drive to the Bonne Terre hospital made the chances for the ebbing lives seem very slim.

For the first time, Donnie wished he could pray. Desperately he searched Harry's face for some reassurance, but he saw that the older man felt as helpless as he did.

Suddenly the sound of the front door opening startled them. Paralyzed, they listened and heard soft voices. Knowledge of possible danger was obvious in the words, spoken between sobs. "Is it safe?" a vague tone subsided. Then other speakers questioned each other, until finally one called out.

"Who's here?" and "Oh, it's you, Donnie," she said with a trace of relief.

Bonds of courage enveloped Mrs. Cole and several neighbor women who had come to stand by until help arrived for the stricken family. As Donnie and Harry turned to leave, the ladies entered the kitchen and hovered over the crushed, bleeding figures.

The men departed through the bullet-riddled screen door

with bowed heads and walked quietly around front to their waiting car. At that point they were hailed by gun-laden Ray Taylor and San Gilliam who said they were searching the area for the criminal *or criminals*.

"Any suspects?" Donnie called as San cautiously approached the store porch.

"No! Any signs up there?" San nodded toward the house.

"Two in the kitchen. Shotgun on the floor — broken." The teen-ager's hoarse voice cracked as he finished, "Some savage raid."

"We're goin' up Trace Creek to look," Donnie continued. "Someone must tell the Kearns, too. Looks like Diane with Jo in the kitchen. Can't tell if they're dead or alive."

While Donnie and Harry left for their destination, San and Ray went to the store. When they left, minutes later, San's elderly face revealed the inner anguish he felt. In stony resolution he walked with a heavier step on his spindly legs and shouldered his rifle forcefully above his rawboned torso. Clutching the hard gunstock in his toil-worn hands, he was as swift-footed as his younger partner, despite his age and waning health.

The old man led the dogged pursuit of the unknown killer — his warm heart aching for his good friends, his tears falling silently.

Murder In The Afternoon

The Capture . . .

As San and Ray walked westward between Cub Creek and the county road, glancing from side to side for clues to the killer's whereabouts, a flood of memories of the dead storekeeper came swooping over San. How many times had he and Lynn Barr stripped a corn patch together? Lynn was, in his estimation, among the finest of men. Never had he heard him utter an unkind word. *Murder? How could it happen to Lynn?*

People used to say, "If ever there was a Christian, Lynn's one!" In all his dealings as a farmer, livestock trader, and businessman, he had always been honest and notably scrupulous. *And how that man could sing!* San remembered the deep bass voice which had caused tremors even in his own hardened heart. Aside from Lynn's conspicuous lack of profanity in recent years, those constant testimonies in song had made the biggest impression in other lives. And what a mainstay Lynn had been to San and his family last spring when their only son Jun had been killed in an accident.

Now the spent old-timer wondered, *Why? Murder? Not Lynn.* He was almost ready to cry out to the Almighty, something he had never done before — in fact, he had scarcely considered the existence of a divine Creator.

Lost in his thoughts, San — and his ally — moved quickly down the roadside, alert to every crackle of underbrush. Neither spoke until they had passed the second fence corner. Then Ray turned onto Cole Road.

"What's that?" he said sharply.

"Where?"

"Over by the spring branch." Ray, the tall and husky partner, was already striding toward the fresh-water pool which many people considered the best tasting water anywhere. Scooping up the shirts from where they hung over the edge of the stream, he turned back to his companion. His dark eyes were fierce, all but leaping from his grim face, as he pointed solemnly to the blood-streaked cloth. Without speaking, they turned and quickened their pace down the road with the bedraggled shirts tucked under Ray's arm.

Over another mile they scrutinized every inch of the vicinity. Then, rounding a bend, they spotted two boys up ahead sauntering along the road as though they had all day and not a care. Striking a connection with the searchers' only clue were the youths' bare backs.

"Stop where you are!" San Gilliam's gruff voice pierced the air as he walked slowly toward them. He and Ray trained their guns on the fidgety pair.

"Put your hands up! High!" San bellowed.

"What d'ya want with us?" the taller youth snarled. On second thought, he offered a toothy grin, then began to swear profusely.

"Quiet!" Ray ordered as he checked their pockets. "You'll be held for questioning."

Before he could tell them why, a cream-colored sedan drove around the curve a few feet from where they were standing. With the left-turn signal flickering, the car pulled up beside the group.

"What's the trouble?" The driver, Marvin Midgett, asked through his open car window. His wife and daughter beside him looked on perplexed, for the driveway of the relatives they'd come to visit was blocked by these gun-laden neighbors apparently holding the shirtless youths at bay.

"Barrs're shot." San looked sidewise briefly. "Lynn's dead!"

"You don't mean it!" Thunderstruck, Marvin stammered, "Why, I — I just talked to him about an hour ago." Incredulously he looked at his watch and then at his daughter. Both remembered seeing these surly youths on their way to the store.

"Shot from behind. Never had a chance! Something bad happened at the house, too." As San finished the description, Mrs. Midgett and Bonnie Sue cried out.

Seizing an opportunity in the interruption, the boys lowered their hands and turned to walk away. The taller one jeered, "You can't do nothin to us!" as he fastened bony fingers in his hip pockets.

A rifle blast overhead stopped them even before San roared, "Keep your hands up — or I'll blow your brains out!" He punctuated the statement with an oath, and they didn't hesitate to comply.

San's sharp chin quivered as he tightened his finger

around the trigger, and there was no doubt in anyone's mind that he meant every word.

Instead of their original twitching and murmuring, the response changed to an arrogant silence, and except for deep, racking breaths they remained statuelike with seeming respect for the armed leader.

Marvin's face was pale from shock, and he finally said something about going to help and drove away.

Guarding warily, Gilliam and Taylor remained silent. The old man's feet were planted firmly on the roadway, and his deep-set eyes, stern and relentless, glared from his chalky face as he assured the two boys, "We'll wait for the police if it takes all night."

Murder In The Afternoon

Jerry . . .

Shortly before 6:00 P.M. that fateful Saturday, Jerry Sadler was in his little black coupe traveling south and pushing a little extra to make it on time for his date with Jo Barr. Turning at the first intersection a mile from his home, he wondered how many times he'd turned here in the two years he and Jo had been dating.

His dad often teased, "Every time I try to drive one of our cars past the intersection of C highway it turns automatically towards Cub Creek."

The distance to the Barr farm no longer seemed great, even though it was eighteen miles, but Jerry's friends couldn't understand his dating someone so far away or his faithfulness to one girl. Guys at college had kidded him often enough, "Look at the *women!* Take a break, man, and live!"

He'd laugh with them and say, "Mine's back home." He'd never been attracted to another girl since he'd met Jo when she was a high school freshman. Vibrant and gay, a petite picture with her dark hair and eyes, she was an exhilarating companion. More than that, though, was the extra spark in her personality, her self-confidence. Not that she was ever haughty, but rather he was impressed by the ease with which she met different situations.

His parents had approved his choice, too, for several reasons. Not the least of these were Jo's older sisters, Glenna Mae and Rosemary, the two tall redheads who were well-known in Potosi. His folks were especially fond of Rosemary. For years they had shopped where she was cashier and assistant manager in the town's largest grocery store. Customers and colleagues often called this young woman "Red," but from the start they knew it wouldn't nettle her. Her winsome personality had won her an outstanding reputation and a host of friends.

Weekends he and Jo spent almost entirely together. Sunday mornings she played the piano for early service at Joseph Chapel near the farm and was also accompanist for the 11:00 worship service at Bethel Church where she sang in a girls' trio and took an active part in youth activities. Jerry went to his own church in the mornings, but by early afternoon he and Jo were together and would join her family for evening services at Bethel.

As he entered the village of Belgrade, Jerry roused from his thoughts to check his speedometer. Main Street was almost deserted except for a car in front of the bank building and one beside the restaurant next door. A short distance ahead he could see someone waving frantically and screaming.

Could she be trying to stop me? he wondered. *Yes, must be!*

Braking sharply, he pulled over to the curb in front of the distraught woman.

"I've been watching for you." Crying, almost hysterically, she blurted, "Something bad's happened at Cub Creek. Valle Barr's been shot. They took her through about fifteen minutes ago. Melvin Taylor told me to call police officers and ambulances, and I'll call your parents, too."

Shocked and anguished at the thought of Jo's probable danger, Jerry drove away, afraid to guess where his journey might end and what he might find when it did.

Where are the others? What happened? His jumbled thoughts raced with his car, skidding around every curve. *Where was Lynn when this happened?* He pictured the big man with his perpetual smile and knew that he'd have been equal to any situation if he were home — *if he were alive!*

Forever was a fitting description for his travel time, and more than that elapsed, it seemed, after he crossed the bridge and headed down that last open stretch where cars lined the road as far as he could see.

From the parking lot he ran through the gate past a sea of faces. Hundreds seemed to be gathered in the yard among the trees. Some people stood out in the lane and others on the graveled lot down front. Their expressions mirrored grief mingled with fear, as though cast in stone. Scarcely a word was spoken.

The front door opened before he reached it, and inside he met another solemn cluster. As he passed a broken shotgun, fear tightened its grip on his heart. Someone was pointing toward the kitchen, so he hurried on.

Jerry   83

That last threshold was like the drop over a precipice. Jerry saw red and bleak despair. For one awful moment he thought he would faint. Then, fighting for control, he bent over Jo's still body and knelt in her blood. Sure that she was dead, he laid his face against her chest and listened while he felt for her pulse. However faint, he detected her breathing.

As he slumped over his unconscious sweetheart, half-praying, half-crying, he felt a soft touch on his shoulder. "Jerry," a woman spoke his name softly.

He recognized the neighbor, Mrs. Cole, and her sympathetic presence gave him strength as she knelt beside him and prayed aloud. Minutes later, he was aware of voices. At first they drifted as from another world. Eventually, though, words penetrated his throbbing mind.

"Do you know who she is?" the woman nearest the stove asked.

"It's Diane isn't it? Jo's best friend?"

"No, Diane's not that tall." Mrs. Midgett's voice was positive though broken by her weeping. "It must be Bobbie Shipp. Bonnie Sue said she was here this afternoon." She and the other neighbor women were beside Bobbie, praying and wishing desperately that they could do something for her.

"It was a sudden attack, for sure," another spoke. "Look's like Valle had this chocolate batter ready for the oven, but—," she broke off.

From the distance came the faint sound of a siren, growing louder as help came closer.

Only when the screaming died with the ambulance engine out front did Jerry stir. The hushed grievers shuffled aside to clear a path for the attendants who were preparing to lift the battered bodies.

Jerry stood beside Jo's stretcher, still holding her wrist,

and when the attendant asked him to ride beside her, he responded with a quick nod. In a last look as he was leaving, Jerry groaned with pity for another sufferer. Amid the group of people in the living room, he noticed a tall, attractive redhead in the big rocking chair by the piano. Jo's sister, Glenna Mae, obviously uncomfortable, was sitting erect, the soft folds of her turquoise dress draped over her full figure.

His heart ached. *She shouldn't be here! Does she realize what's happening?*

Then he helped ease the stretcher out the back door and through the yard to the emergency vehicle. Even before the motor started, he began clearing Jo's throat to help her breathe while he pleaded with God and begged her to live through the longest journey of his life.

Murder In The Afternoon

Glenna Mae . . .

Trying to ignore the siren's wail now diminishing into the distance, Glenna Mae McClain sat in her parents' living room. Staunch as her weary back would allow, she braced against the slatted chair frame. While she quietly searched the faces of the people in the room, her slender fingers were busily tracing the rounded chair arms.

A woman sitting nearby talked incessantly about the heat and other trivial subjects, attempting to divert her attention from the suspenseful lull. Glenna managed rational answers to the compassionate person even while her subconscious was flinging questions, *What's going on here? Why all these people? Where's mom? Jo?*

From the moment she'd arrived, this solemn reception had

baffled her. Old friends and casual acquaintances had nodded to her as she slowly entered the room a few minutes earlier. So overwhelming was the shock of seeing this unexplained crowd, that she had taken the first vacant chair.

Now she swayed rhythmically in the sturdy old rocker whose solid foundation was the most soothing of the household effects grouped among the maze of people.

Not a hint of her inner turmoil was reflected in the young mother's face. As always, Glenna was a picture of serenity, attractive in the turquoise checked dress she'd designed for herself. Tiny pleats flowing from the pattern-stitched yoke made a graceful allowance for her full figure. Tall, like Rosemary her older sister, Glenna was poised even at this late stage in her pregnancy.

Because of her coppery shaded hair and sunny nature, she, too, was frequently called "Redhead." These weren't the only features common to the two sisters, however. Inherent in their make-up was that same dauntless courage notable in their parents, Lynn and Valle Barr. Being reared in an enthusiastic atmosphere of working toward eternal goals had prepared the daughters well, and even in times of stress they could draw from their abundance of inspiration and plucky wisdom to meet any crisis head-on.

Still, beyond Glenna's experience was this eerie shift in scenes — this formidable silence. As if in a freakish dream, she was with these people like an actor on an unfamiliar set without lines. A horrible dread hedged her in, and she wanted to cry out her suppressed questions. *But who would answer?* These bystanders looked so bewildered, so tense. She detected teardrops on many of the faces. In the front foyer a youngster whispered and pulled at his mother's skirt, but the woman quickly shushed the child as she stooped to pick him up.

Occasionally Glenna's memory touched a consoling note from Scripture as she was forced to endure the interminable waiting. More than once she recalled the phrase she'd often interpreted for her own two children. "Hang on!" Her challenge was, "Be gristly!" Thus repeating and explaining as situations required, she'd led their first steps in learning of confidence in the Master who rallied His followers with, *In your patience, triumph!*

Now it was the young mother's turn to cling to something, and she knew God was her only real support. Although she couldn't escape the fearful clutches of the unknown, this message was balm to her languished spirit. Thus, she was drawn closer to the Mighty Comforter, whose sublime overture was written by His apostle: "Let Him have all your worries and cares, for He is always thinking about you and watching everything that concerns you." Then, as the high beam of His love penetrated, she tried some of her own advice. Words reechoed from a recent conversation when she'd urged a troubled friend, "Hand in your problem." She'd added quickly, "And leave it there!"

In the young mother's temperament, it was her sheer mettle that most supported her husband and her family. Her resilience in the face of overwhelming circumstances had caused her dad to marvel. "That Gen bounces right back," he'd say, grinning, his dark eyes brimming with pride and admiration. "Nothing fazes her!"

She wondered what dad would say now. She wondered again and again where he was. In the store? Not likely. When Frank had parked down by the road they couldn't even see whether the store door was open because of the wall of people and vehicles forming a barrier around the building. One look at the faces of friends and strangers alike deprived her of a voice for questions, and she'd moved through the crowded parking lot and front yard straight to the house.

Now that endless tramp seemed eons ago instead of minutes. Choking a wild impulse to dart through the maze of people and out the door, she shook herself and sighed tremulously.

With another deep shuddering breath, she forced eyelids open wide and once more began probing the fearful expressions of the petrified figures around her. Even though her vision was blurring the images, she tried to focus on the family portrait above the mantel. Needing the warmth from their smiles, she studied the faces individually.

There was dad, tall and good-looking and eminently worthy the honor paid him as head of the home. His black hair was smoothed back from his high forehead. A relaxed grin of pleasure and affectionate pride corresponded to the perpetual gleam in his dark eyes.

Mother, too, looked natural, like she'd just stopped sewing to greet someone. Silvery hair curled softly above her gentle smile. At the same time her strength was spelled in the willful set of her trim, erect figure.

The tall vivacious redheads, Rosemary and herself, had been single at the time of that photo. Alike in frame and features, they differed in degrees of coloring and make-up. Rosemary's hair, a deep shade of auburn, was shoulder-length and arranged in careful curls. While her expression was smiling and genial, her dark eyes glowed with deep feeling and alert sensitivity.

The nonchalant teen-ager at that family setting, Bonnie, had features most like dad's. Fluffing down across her slender shoulders, her long dark hair was brushed back accentuating her deep widow's peak. The debonair smile and tilt of her chin were no camouflage for her real disposition — modesty in a degree akin to shyness. Even in this light mood, hers was a thoughtful expression that could become suddenly pensive. Her luminous eyes reflected her soft heart that had won her the title "friend of the loser."

Nestled between mother and dad was little sister Jo, just six at the time of that picture. Her nut-brown hair was braided, and the two pigtails tied with red checkered ribbons dangled to her waistline. That crinkled nose and her usual impish grin reflected her utter mischievousness. The whole family doted on her, the youngest. Small wonder she'd been completely spoiled.

Fading out, the family images were so lifelike, yet so far removed. Glenna couldn't restrain the flow of tears. She wondered about Frank. *Is he asking people what's happened? Does anyone know?*

Involuntarily she turned to look out the windows but with no comprehension of the view. Restless, she leaned on one arm, then the other, and finally reached for her mother's ecru and tawny afghan. Homespun textured, its touch was a reminder of her mother's presence. After stroking the familiar weave, Glenna methodically refolded and draped the soft coverlet back over the magazine basket beside the armchair.

W eird though it was to see this horde of people here, she counted it nothing but preposterous that *she'd* be out home at this particular time.

She'd been frying chicken when Frank came home from his office late that afternoon. He'd teased playfully, "Those from grandma's flock?" Then he whistled, lifting the lid of her black iron skillet, "Hey! Look at those drumsticks!"

He sat down and propped his feet on an ottoman, chuckling, "No average birds does your mother raise. Eh?"

"Say," he added, "I need to run out and put a tube in their TV. Wanna take a ride out there?" She knew he didn't mean it. As she glanced sideways from the browning chicken pieces she'd just turned, she caught his boyish grin.

"Why, yes. That's just what I need — a nice, long ride," she tossed back, surprising him.

"Now, honey, do you really think you should? After all, you could go into labor any minute."

"Guess we could go to the hospital from there. I'm ready. Am I!"

She'd finished preparing the meal, including the luscious fried chicken, but it would be a long time before she could endure the pungent aroma of crunchy golden fryers in a hot skillet. That was to be her memory's vivid connection to today's bloodstained events.

Waiting, near the edge of her chair now, Glenna was thankful that Frank's parents had come by to take their two youngsters to a carnival. This was certainly no place for them, although they had suitcases packed and were eager for their stay here while she was in the hospital.

Shaken from her reminiscing by the insistent thumps of her soon-to-be-born infant, Glenna looked at her watch. Had it stopped? She put it against her ear. *So few minutes had passed!*

She ventured a brief glance over her shoulder, wondering what was happening in the kitchen. There was a crowd in there, too, and *something red?* She determined not to look back again. Instead, she looked out the window with deeper concentration.

The bridge! Still in place, of course. That prominent

landmark was a steely bulwark. Crossing it minutes ago she'd gasped in surprise, "What's going on?"

"Look at the cars!" Frank whistled long and low at the endless row of cars lining the roadside to the store and beyond.

The sound of his awe shocked her like a bombshell, for the first car she sighted was right in front of the store. *Out of place.* That was certainly the family car. Then she'd noticed that dad's truck was parked in its usual spot in the lane at the corner of the yard fence.

Remembering that now, she supposed dad wasn't in the city. But then he rarely went on Saturday.

Could Jo be gone on her date? Glenna checked the time, painfully aware of its standstill. *Was Jerry's car out front?* She strained to recall that first glimpse of the parking area and whether the familiar black coupe was parked by the gate. Her deep study was futile. By the time she'd moved through that conglomeration of vehicles and thronged people, nothing was recognizable.

Pushing back a wall of tears and despair, she again fastened her gaze on the bridge structure. She remembered watching from these same windows when she was Jo's age and waiting for her boyfriend. She could almost expect to see Frank's car coming off the slab bridge-base and down the road. Instead, what she saw coming from the crossing filled her with new dread.

Before she saw it, she heard the screaming siren, and a flashing red light swept past the iron railings on the old bridge. Then the blue highway patrol car emerged from the green overgrown archway and raced down the pavement between strings of cars.

A knot in her throat was choking her, and at the same time the baby's threshing made it unbearable to sit still. She stood up and waited a few seconds to recover her balance, then began her slow walk to the front windows.

Wide-eyed, she peered at the storefront where a thick-set man walked over from the roadside and hailed the patrolman who'd just stopped. Glenna couldn't make out the few chopped words she heard the man call, but she realized the urgency when he pointed his rifle barrel down the road.

As the patrolman stepped from his car, Glenna knew immediately who he was. Uncle Herman, her dad's younger brother, tall, walking erect. Except for his uniform, she could have mistaken him for her father. People moved aside to clear his path to the store, and he made straight for the door and went in without once breaking his stride.

In minutes, Glenna saw him come back outside. His head was bowed, but momentarily he straightened and walked back to the patrol car with his usual decisive step, motioning for the rifle-bearing messenger, who Glenna now realized was Ray Taylor, to get in beside him.

Watching the two car doors close, Glenna stifled a notion to cry out, "Wait!" and ask her uncle, "What's it all about?"

Another patrol car drove down from the bridge, stopped briefly by the store, and then followed her uncle, while Glenna remained transfixed by the front window trying to analyze the scene before her. It reminded her of an ancient painting where a host of mourners awaited the final dirge. She longed to brush the figures from the canvas and replace them with her loved ones who belonged here.

With great relief, she saw Frank coming through the gate and up to the house. She met him at the front door.

"Let's go." His gentle strength was comforting as he took

her arm, and they walked slowly back to the car.

He'd turned the car around and was driving away when he spoke again. "We'll go to the hospital." He said it softly but matter-of-factly.

Trusting his discretion, she held her questions and rode quietly, sitting close to her husband all the way.

At the Bonne Terre hospital, Frank said simply, "I'll be back soon, dear."

She waited in the car, watching the friendly hospital lights glow into the gathering darkness while Frank disappeared through the main entrance to the building. It was good to have a hospital this close, she reflected, and for its size this was one of the best. Not equipped to care for the more critical cases, it was still able to give emergency aid before transferring patients to one of the St. Louis hospitals.

Glenna guessed that her husband was going to find her obstetrician, but she was too dazed to wonder why. She was waiting, quietly composed, when Frank returned, but the minute he got in the car she knew his news was bad. He bit his lower lip twice and swallowed painfully. Then he plunged into the awful story. Her doctor had advised him to tell her right away, he said.

First he told her that mother and Jo were getting emergency treatment but were still unconscious. Frank had to stop and clear his throat before he could tell the ghastliest details: her father had been shot to death in the store and Bobbie Lou Shipp, who had been brutally beaten, was dead-on-arrival at the hospital.

Glenna was shaking, not fully comprehending it yet. Frank put his arms around her and said quickly, "I called Lee and Rosemary." He choked up and lowered his head over the steering wheel while Glenna stared in disbelief.

Glenna Mae 97

Finally she whispered, "Did they know about it yet?"

"Sadler family came — told them." He straightened and looked out into the gathering darkness. "Two suspects were picked up down the road from the farm. Two boys — they confessed!"

Glenna sat stunned. She tried to talk and couldn't. Except for the insistent jostling inside her mid-section, she felt lifeless.

"Murdered!" Frank repeated abruptly as he turned the car key. She flinched at the rasp of the starting motor.

Continuing, Frank's voice was husky. "Let's go over to Rosemary and Lee's house now. Bill and Bonnie are on the way."

She thought how right it was to share this grief with her sisters, although it would take several hours for Bonnie and her husband to travel from the Chicago, Illinois, area. Further thought was too heartrending.

Mother? Would she live? And dad's gone — gone?

What about the baby of the family? Jo had been so vibrant just yesterday at their home, talking and laughing. And now? *Would she survive?*

Frank waited until they were almost at her sister's home near Potosi before he prepared her for what she was to find. Rosemary had been unconscious since the horrible news came, and Bonnie was under sedation on the long ride home.

In that moment, Glenna let go. Tears flowed down her face and fell to dampen her smocked bodice. Then with a shuddering sigh, she once more released the burden, her breaking heart and new concern for her unborn infant, to the lamblike Sufferer who had always carried her before.

Murder In The Afternoon

The Hospital . . .

While countless friends and relatives streamed through the entrance and into the main lobby of the Bonne Terre hospital that July evening, the chief of staff was beginning a conference with one member of the Barr family.

Margaret Barr, wife of state patrolman Herman Barr, Lynn's brother, had been paged and had hurried from the waiting room to the doctor's office. Now seated before his desk, she waited. Looking into his face beneath the silver-streaked dark hair, she tried to read hope in his expression, but none showed in his solemn gray eyes.

"I'm sorry," he said. "I would never give you false hope. We're doing all that's possible, but I'm afraid we can't save them." He ended with an ominous finality.

"You understand they can't be moved?" he explained.

"Yes," her voice barely sounded through the stricture that was her throat.

He took a deep breath and continued. "The girl has a severe concussion, and her skull is fractured in so many — well, the right backside of her head looks like a crushed eggshell."

He paused as the impact of his words showed in the pallor of Margaret's face.

"We'd move her to a St. Louis hospital and a neurologist, but we'll have to wait and see. Maybe in twenty-four hours — if she's alive." There was no optimism in his voice.

"And Valle?" The sister-in-law tightened her arms around her body as though bracing herself for the answer.

"Odds aren't in her favor either. One shell cut through her right shoulder. Her left thumb's gone. The shot pellets are scattered all over her body — her legs, arms. But there are also hundreds of shot and metal slivers under her scalp. One's lodged at the corner of her eye." Miserably he looked down at his scarred desk top. "But the most crucial factor — they've lost too much blood!"

Margaret leaned back from the edge of her chair where she'd unconsciously moved closer to the bulk of his desk. She waited quietly, almost as if she hadn't heard him until he was halfway through the next sentence.

"They have the same type blood, and it's rare — none available. At least — they need several pints immediately."

"Doctor, my husband will have it rushed from the city. Herman can radio —."

"I'm afraid you don't understand," he broke in. "The nearest supply is in Kansas City. It might as well be in Europe. They need it now!" he emphasized, whacking the desk with an open palm. "Otherwise the brain damage will be —." His words trailed off as he hesitated to tell the whole story. Starting again, his voice was gruff with concern. "Even if they live, they'll be blank as that wall." He pointed with his right index finger.

Crestfallen, Margaret dropped back on her chair, a picture of despair, staring down at her hands as if in a trance.

"There's a slight chance," the doctor's tone was even, not promising. "I've called local radio stations to broadcast an urgent bulletin. Telephone operators are relaying the message. But to find enough people with this type soon enough?" He shook his head.

"Thank you, doctor." Margaret rose to leave.

Dazed, she moved down the corridor past throngs of bewildered people who were waiting for some sign of hope.

"How could this happen?" a pained voice asked. "To such kind people. Why?"

Approaching the emergency wing, Margaret found the waiting room as crowded as the hallways. In the chair nearest the nurses' station sat a forlorn young man whose profile looked familiar to her. His blond head rested on his trembling hands.

"Jerry?" she spoke his name softly. The heartbroken youth stood up and hurried to meet her.

She was horrified at the sight of the red streaks on his face and his bloody clothes, especially the light summer slacks which were red from the knees down. His arms went out and enfolded her. Shuddering, he clung to her for a moment before he poured out his heart.

He told of the nightmarish ride to the hospital: praying, hoping, feebly trying to keep Jo alive. Battling impossible odds, he'd held her head and cleared her mouth and nose to help her breathing. Even though he doubted that she could hear his words, he'd begged her to "Hang on — please. Please live."

Hope had all but vanished when the siren failed twenty-five miles from Bonne Terre, and the red flasher was useless as a warning signal.

"Traffic just wouldn't stop!" Jerry moaned.

"Does Joe know about Bobbie yet?" Margaret asked. Bobbie's boyfriend was her cousin, and she had been wondering about him.

"Joe just left," Jerry said, telling her of his deep concern for his good friend who had come into the emergency entrance right behind the ambulance.

"Joe, Ralph, and Diane were waiting for Jo, Bobbie, and me in Belgrade. We were supposed to triple-date. They waited and waited. When they saw the ambulance and patrol cars go screaming past towards Cub Creek, they decided to drive out that way. The ambulance was just pulling out of the farm when they got there, so they turned around and followed it. Joe's so torn up," Jerry whispered.

He heaved a sigh as he saw his mother coming down the hall. Sara Sadler had brought clean clothing for her son, although he hadn't even noticed that he was blood-stained. Neither did Margaret realize, until hours later, that on her back the white linen fabric was stained with two red handprints.

Darker than the night outside was the density of gloom enshrouding those who clustered in the hospital waiting rooms. Hope was low as the long vigil began, and one after another the Barr relatives joined Margaret. But no one was allowed to see either of the unconscious survivors.

The terrible silence, broken only by the crying, personified death hanging like a pall in the lonely place. No one spoke, but the racking sobs were more graphic than any utterance. Myriad questions had already been asked. There were no answers. No answers to the "why" of this senseless slaughter.

Into the night, lines of prospective blood donors moved in to be typed and, if possible, contribute that rare substance. Last to come, in answer to the appeal, was a robust trooper, friend and associate of Herman Barr. His blood type was compatible, and the amount he was able to give completed the essential eight pints that Valle and Jo needed.

Time was at a minimum, for most of Valle's veins had collapsed. In efforts to administer the lifeblood infusion, the doctors were forced to slash her arms, ankles, thighs, and finally her groins before they found an open channel that would take the precious flood.

Doctors kept the relatives informed of developments, but they also warned that the transfusions might not have come soon enough. Though x-rays showed an image much like a freckled complexion on the back of Valle's head where shot and metal slivers underlaid her whole scalp, the wave clamps in her hair apparently had acted as a buffer to scatter the shot and save her life.

By 2:00 A.M., Margaret and her sister-in-law, Gerene Barr, decided on a hurried trip home to prepare sleeping arrangements for other relatives who kept arriving during the night. This would surely be a grueling day for the family. Some would stay at the hospital, while others would take care of funeral details. And the livestock and farm on Cub Creek would need attention.

When Margaret and Gerene returned to the hospital, they were told that there had been no visible change in the two victims, but that the anxious family could now see their loved ones.

Jerry stayed beside Jo's bed, while his parents and sister took turns sitting with him. Ever watchful, they tried to detect any movement or change in her breathing. Helplessly they watched the red seeping to the edges of her white skull-swathing.

Though the doctors gave them no reason to believe Jo would ever wake, Jerry constantly watched her closed eyelids, hoping and praying that she'd look at him soon. Had he known the number of nights he would spend like this one, he might have questioned his endurance.

Murder In The Afternoon

The Motive . . .

On Sunday, newspapers across the nation carried glaring headlines.

"MAD DOG" KILLER ADMITS SHOOTING AND BEATING FOUR

In the Washington County Jail in Potosi, two young criminals bemoaned their fate. Nineteen-year-old Hank Jones and fourteen-year-old Jim Banks cursed the bad luck that had caused their capture. Being caught seemed their only regret.

While Jones admitted the plan to kill the storekeeper and his family, Banks denied taking part in the crime, although he admitted being on the scene.

"Guess I'm nothing but a dummy, and we pulled the

wrong ropes yesterday," Jones was quoted as saying to an interviewer.

On Monday the burning heat scorched the backs of Jones and Banks as they returned to the Barr farm with the patrolmen and county sheriff. There were no dry threads in any of their clothing as they stood by the shimmering water of Cub Creek while a crew of men probed the rocky bed in the spot where the boys said they had hurled Barr's key ring.

From that sweltering bank the silent, stone-faced youths were taken to the store and then to the house where they reenacted the malicious killings and beatings. Except for Jones's involuntary twitching and an occasional pat on his bare head, he was as unruffled as his younger partner. It wasn't until he demonstrated how he'd jerked off his hat and slammed it on the floor that his expression was transformed. Suddenly belligerent, he furiously stomped the floor where the floppy gray headgear had been smashed during the crime. The evening newspapers listed this outburst as his last show of emotion and what the sheriff termed, "The single most hostile point in this confession."

One of the largest newspapers in the state carried the details of the crime and quoted the state's prosecutor as saying: "It defies comprehension that a crime should be committed with such savagery with no more motive."

For a motive had been established. Jones and Banks had merely "wanted a car."

T hat blistering Monday was the first of many court proceedings. After the group returned from the murder scene, Jones was taken to his first hearing where a complaint was filed and charges read to him while he chewed gum and stared out the window, showing little emotion.

According to Jones's confession, he and Banks had followed a prearranged plan to divert Barr's attention by ordering a bologna sandwich in order to shoot him and steal money and his car to "Go out and have a big time." His statement revealed a rational, although criminal, scheme to commit a robbery of a store in an isolated area and to murder the proprietor's family in order to eliminate potential witnesses.

In another part of the confession he stated that they drank six or eight bottles of 3.2 percent beer as they finished the planning. At that point, he claimed, they were "feeling good," so they started toward the isolated store in an old junk car which they were soon forced to abandon. They walked over twelve miles in the burning sun to complete their ghastly work.

Nineteen-year-old Jones was charged with first degree murder in connection with Barr's death. A motion was also filed Monday afternoon by the state's attorney asking that Jim Banks be transferred from the juvenile jurisdiction and tried as an adult. Following the initial confessions, the fourteen-year-old had maintained a stony silence. His only statement was that he hadn't been in any previous trouble, although by Monday he had admitted taking part in the plan to get money and a car to "have a big time."

On Tuesday the second charge of premeditated murder was given Jones in connection with the death of Bobbie Lou Shipp. He had yet to receive two attempted murder charges and the attempted robbery charge.

Authorities soon learned that Jones had three burglary

charges pending in another county. In fact, the trial in that location had been scheduled for this same week, but the prosecutor said it would be postponed, not interfering with the Potosi proceedings.

The juvenile officers filed a charge alleging Banks delinquent by reason of murder and a motion requesting the case be certified to the county court and the defendant tried as an adult. Both boys were being held without bail.

W hile the confessed criminals cursed their fate, a multitude of friends and relatives grieved with the two stricken families. Two mortuaries in the same county were filled and overflowing with flowers and mourners on that hot, dismal Monday.

At any minute two more could die. Jo Barr was still in a coma and was being rushed by ambulance to St. Luke's Hospital in St. Louis where she would be treated by a reputable neurologist. Valle Barr was in critical condition in the Bonne Terre hospital.

By Tuesday morning people were waiting in line to pay their respects at the funeral home and at the Shipp home to the two whose lives had been "snuffed out."

One a vivacious and talented seventeen-year-old who had been loved by many. "She was an active member of the church and a leader in all its organizations and choir activities."

The other a fifty-six-year-old businessman and farmer loved in the county. He had been an elected officer in the county court — associate judge and presiding judge — for twelve consecutive years. "In the business world his integrity was unchallenged. He lived by the roadside and was a friend to man."

On Tuesday Valle Barr was conscious for a brief period after being semiconscious for twenty-four hours. On Sunday she'd heard a voice through the fog saying, "Jo's here." She'd clung to the words in hazy relief. That must mean alive. *Alive? Who's alive?* One time she heard a gruff whisper, "Caught them."

Edges of cruel memory came slicing into awareness with the needle-sharp metal chips and shot pressed against her skull. The hours passed unmarked until that Tuesday midday when she realized two friends were with her.

No one mentioned Lynn, and she couldn't bring herself to ask about him. She couldn't bear the answer. For through all the haziness surrounding her, in her subconscious lurked an inkling of the procession now winding its way across the peaceful countryside.

Like a long chain of tokens, the funeral cortege following the regal white hearse wound its way through the hills and entered the peaceful valley where the Barr family had been so violently uprooted.

The store looked lonely and deserted. No one had hung out the familiar sign —

STORE CLOSED — FOR FUNERAL
Back at 3:00
L.B.

Murder In The Afternoon

Part 2 . . .
Ella Jo . . .

An expanse of white was my first perception. Walls, ceiling, the very air I breathed was colorless. This room with its antiseptic smells and sounds was my world. I had no knowledge how long I had been here nor did I wonder — or care. For I couldn't remember any other place.

At first I could only discern tiny circles of light and sometimes a face alternating with scenes of dark and horrible places. Who would help me escape from those dungeons? Sometimes they were deep, sooty pits, sometimes confining concrete walls, and always they were alive with crawling foot-long insects and vile creatures.

Someone wished, "Happy birthday!" and I was surprised. My head ached and I couldn't remember what "birthday" meant.

There were no days or nights — just long expanses of unbroken time.

A hazy awareness of a flavor invaded my long sleep. I yearned for it, but did not know what to call the tangy nectar I craved. Then with no knowledge of having spoken, I was sipping the luscious juice from a glass someone held.

I could hear soft, soothing voices, sometimes singing, and I knew Jerry was beside me. I said his name sometimes.

Finally the tormented times diminished, and I became vaguely aware of life around me. I began to watch the people who were with me, asking and wondering where I was and why.

Rosemary and Lee came, and I asked them about mom and dad. I couldn't understand why they hadn't been to see me. Their answers didn't sound convincing. They said the folks were busy with haying season, but I knew my parents would never neglect me for a hay crop.

During those days my fingers kept searching restlessly for something. Finally one day I said wistfully, not even realizing what I was saying, "My piano." Then Jerry and my cousins realized that I was searching for that which had been such a vital part of my life.

Before I knew what was happening, they had me in a wheelchair. This was the first time I remembered being up. They wheeled me down a hall and settled me on a hard seat before an object that looked vaguely familiar.

Everything was a blurry mass of black and white and the touch of cool keys. I didn't even know what I was playing. My head felt enormous, but lighter than air, and I was nauseated. I didn't recall the trip back to the room, but later I begged my uncle to take me back to play again, and I asked him what song I had played.

I felt the bandages on my head and asked, "What

happened to my head?" My tongue found the sliver of my front tooth — it was a weird sensation — and I wanted to know how it had become broken.

"Probably something fell and hit your head," was the unsatisfactory answer. So I kept asking, "What hit me?"

"We don't know."

One day I thought I'd found a clue. "Oh, I think I know what it was. The last thing I remember —."

Jerry and the others seemed to be watching me closely.

"Sewing. It was one day after school. I bet the sewing table fell on my head." My head ached as I puzzled over it.

"Maybe," was their only answer.

People seemed to be showering me with gifts and mail. Unsigned packages came with every kind of gift imaginable. I couldn't understand the amount of mail and visitors. Friends came long distances — even an evangelist from northern Illinois who had stayed in our home. Everyone — except mother and dad.

One day Jerry left me for the first time. He said he was going home for something, but after he left I was terrified. Nothing was clear to me, but I had such a vague lost feeling. My window overlooked the parking lot, and although I could still see only dim outlines, I stared out the window, fitfully watching for him to return and quizzing my companions all day. "Where is he? Isn't it time for Jerry to come back?"

What tremendous relief I felt when he returned, and I threw my arms around him. He held me close, and I didn't ever want him to let me go.

A few days later, for the first time I spent the night alone. Until then Jerry had sat in a chair all night near my bed. But the doctors had suggested that I was well enough to be alone.

Ella Jo   119

Those nights were terrible. I felt so alone, so uneasy, in a way I couldn't describe. Nor could I describe the apparitions outside my windows.

I was sure a creature was out there in the dark shadows. *A creature with a gun!*

By the middle of August I was recovering miraculously, although I still wasn't aware of much around me. I could sit up for short periods and could walk a few steps with help and support. But my daily improvement was fraught with disquieting questions. I was becoming more and more distressed because I couldn't remember what had happened to my head, and no one seemed to know anything about it. So many cards and visitors, and yet they'd have me believe it was only a minor accident?

There still was no sign of my parents nor a word from them, except that someone brought a small jewelry box from home. "It's the watch your mom and dad ordered for your birthday. Don't you remember picking it out last month?" cousin Gereldene asked me.

No, I didn't remember anything about a watch, but I let them put it on my wrist and wore it proudly. Once I told someone, "It's for my birthday — from mom and dad." But I was so confused. Why didn't they come? Somehow I knew all was not well. Things like the story about hay season being the reason they hadn't come just didn't ring true. Anyway, I could only concentrate on the problem for a few minutes at a time. The hard part was that I couldn't

remember when I'd last seen them. I tried so hard to
remember.

Visibly troubled, I surprised Jerry one morning shortly
after he arrived at the hospital.

"I had a weird dream — sometime — so real, and yet —,"
I was vague. "Not last night. Really, I don't know when
it was."

"Oh?" Jerry answered casually.

"Well, I was lying on the floor, and — someone was
with me." I thought awhile. "Maybe it was Aunt Gerene.
She had dark hair — like mine." I strained to remember
the details.

"Where were you?"

"It was a dark room. So — o — o dreary!" I shuddered and
closed my eyes.

"Any furniture?"

"A table. Long dark wooden. It was so big and ugly! Had
splinters sticking out all over it."

"And someone was with you?"

"Yes, I remember that. The table was on one side of me
and she was lying by my other side."

"Anything else?"

"She was screaming!"

Other images, which I referred to as dreams, came to
my mind the next day.

"Do you know Donnie Compton?" I asked Jerry.

"I've seen him."

"Sometime I dreamed about him too. I don't know when.
His face was close." I finished in a monotone reflecting the
strange and real sensation. "Isn't that odd? Just his face
close-up?"

"Yes, I guess so," Jerry said strangely.

"Doesn't anyone know what hit me?" I'd repeat the

question at intervals as I touched the edge of my topknot bandages. I could see a hazy impression of myself in a mirror and detected the color of my bruised face.

Each day Jerry took a leisurely time and read my stack of mail to me. But one morning a late letter was brought to me when Jerry and everyone else had left the room temporarily.

Straining my eyes, I managed to read the name signed and a scrawled sentence, *I sent your mother a card, too.* I puzzled over the message, and my head ached from reading the few words. Two things were beyond me. This was from a woman I barely knew, and why should she send mom a card?

When Jerry came back, I showed it to him. "Look at this. Sure sounds funny, doesn't it?"

"Oh, she probably wrote your mom to say that she's sorry you're in the hospital." His answer sounded flimsy.

"Maybe so."

Another vivid incident from the past flashed through my mind that week. This time I knew it wasn't a dream, although I couldn't guess how long ago it had happened.

On a summer afternoon I'd been browsing through a catalog selecting fabrics for my fall wardrobe. Sitting there in the front porch swing, I'd planned some plaid wool skirts and some solid colors, gold with brown threads interwoven, and a scarlet tweed. These I chose to complement my sweater collection, and a charcoal suit ensemble would be the versatile addition to round out the picture. I'd thumbed the pages finding dressmaker patterns, figured the material yardages, and, with mother's okay, made the order.

The white atmosphere with its medicinal scents was replaced by the aura of homey comfort under blue sky and summer sun. I breathed the fragrance of woodland and glistening lawn after a shower and began to cry. Jerry asked why.

"I didn't get my sewing done." My eyes were brimming with tears.

Gereldene was there to reassure me. "You'll still have time before school. Aunt Valle and your sisters will help you when you get home."

But that wasn't the real problem. I wanted to cry in frustration — not about sewing, but about home. It was like *home* wasn't there any more.

My cousin Gereldene was like a sister, and just her presence was a consolation to me. I was overjoyed when they told me I would be able to leave the hospital and stay with Gereldene and her husband. The doctor said it would be better than making the long trip home right away.

On the fateful morning that I was to leave the hospital for the first time, I was excited. I could hardly wait through the extensive examination and the doctor's questioning routine. "Does this hurt? Touch the dot. Right eye closed. Left. Touch your nose. Which of these objects is larger? Closer?" And on and on. It seemed I'd never get away.

Then they were helping me into a wheelchair and rolling it

down to the lobby and outside to the waiting car.

Leaving the security of my small world, the hospital room and constant care, I asked what day it was, although it meant nothing to me. Time had stopped. Now my head ached, and the great excitement of anticipation was fading. The sun was much too bright.

Being in the big city of St. Louis had always thrilled me, especially after I'd planned to come here to college next year. Now, riding through it, even the metropolis had no appeal. Like the rest of my world, it was unreal.

The trip was like another dream. My head felt too light, so I rested on Jerry's shoulder, overwhelmingly glad that he was with me. Every few minutes he asked how I felt, and I managed a smile as I opened my eyes to the giddy world. I hadn't realized how weak I still was. By the time we got to Gereldene's house, I was so weary I had to go to bed.

Late in the afternoon I was rested and sitting up again. Little did I know what those next moments would reveal!

Propped comfortably in a cushioned lounge with Jerry close beside me, I was at ease, looking at the circle of family seated around me. Gereldene and her husband, Aunt Gerene, Uncle Roy, and Mariam, another cousin. Looking at Uncle Roy, I thought how much like dad he was — tall with broad shoulders, although uncle's hair was gray. As I looked from one face to another, all were quiet for a few seconds.

"Honey, we have something to tell you," Gereldene said in a voice as calm as her face. "About those dreams you were remembering in the hospital —."

"Yes?"

"We must tell you they were partly true." Her voice was soft, controlled.

I was thoughtful, remembering the dream. "On the floor?"

"Yes."

"And Aunt Gerene was with me — screaming?"

"You were on the floor, but it was someone else with you." Aunt Gerene helped. "Do you remember Bobbie Lou Shipp, your friend?"

"I haven't seen her for a long time. Before school was out."

"She spent a weekend with you this summer. Remember?"

"No." I felt limp.

"It was while she was visiting you that Saturday afternoon that you were hurt," Gereldene continued. "You were lying on the floor together because two boys came in with a gun. Remember them?"

I shook my head. "No." But I stiffened at the mention of the gun.

"Your mother is in the Bonne Terre hospital. She was shot twice, but she's doing well, and she'll probably be able to go home to Rosemary's by the time you can make the trip to Potosi."

"Where were we?" My knuckles whitened as I gripped the chair arms.

"You girls were in the kitchen, and you were both hit on the head. Bobbie didn't live very long."

"Dad?" I whispered, as if the answer were too obvious.

"He was in the store. They shot and killed him first."

It was finished at last — the answers I had been groping for so desperately. I moved my fingers slightly, then clasped them in my lap as I looked from face to face for a clue. Did *they* believe it? *Was it true?*

"Oh — hurts!" I said, staring at nothing. I knew they were telling the truth, but I couldn't remember. I couldn't cry. Why cry over a *dream* — a nightmare?

I was quiet for a long time. A time when my family, though only a remnant, wove me into a security of love that made all the difference as I struggled to accept something I couldn't comprehend.

During the following days I began to learn and assimilate all that had been happening around me in the past weeks. Even my memories of the time in the hospital were vague, and I became aware of things I had not realized at the time.

With the rest of the family, Jerry gave me all the time I needed to absorb the new knowledge and discussed it only as I wanted to. I swayed between the awful truth and the world of suspense. It was like waking from a nightmare, only to find that it was reality.

The family told me that the doctor had at first thought I would not live. Later he had thought it likely that I'd not have my eyesight or my sanity, or that I might be paralyzed.

During the first two weeks in the hospital it had taken two people around the clock to hold me in bed. They had begged the doctor not to put restraints on me as they felt it would make me more uncomfortable. During the second week I had talked in what they thought was a semi-conscious state, although most of my words hadn't made sense. The doctor had prepared them to expect this, warning them of my memory block. Thus, they were not surprised when I rambled on about long past events, apparently reliving certain happy occasions.

Two weeks after the attack I had regained a hazy consciousness. My face was still a purple mask, dark and swollen from the massive bruises, and my head was swathed in the turbanlike bandages. My features were distorted and my eyes looked like red glass balls. In fact, they said my sister Bonnie had fainted at her first sight of me.

To those nearest me — Jerry, Aunt Gerene, and her daughter Gereldene, together with other friends and relatives who came alternately and waited day after day (my sisters were caring for mother in Bonne Terre) — that period had been touch and go. By turns they soothed and sang softly, for the doctor wanted me kept as quiet as possible and surrounded by loved ones.

For days I fought the air over my bed. Aunt Gerene's face hurt long after the stinging slaps she felt leaning over me as I flailed my arms, crying, "Oh! My head!" when I must have been reliving the pounding gun stock. Gereldene had bruises on her shoulders where I'd gripped her trying to pull up from the bed. Her husband, when he could be there, was gentle, yet strong, and capable of calming my harrowing cycles of wild thrashing.

At the end of the two weeks I began having more restful periods and less of the tormented tossing and wrestling with whoever came near. I began following their movements with my eyes when I wasn't in deep sleep.

The neurologist had given explicit orders that I must not be told what had happened. Talk about the bloodshed was forbidden, even in a whisper. He said there was a chance I would overhear, even in my coma. A great mental disturbance or possibly a personality change would occur if I learned the truth before I was ready for it. "Healing of her mind must proceed at its own rate. To force the memory would cause dire repercussions. I could only predict a complete mental breakdown," he had said.

But the time finally came when I began asking about mother and dad — asking questions they couldn't answer — and describing my dreams that bordered so closely on reality. Jerry read and censored all my mail, except for the one card that had slipped through to me.

The day I had been searching so restlessly for the piano, the doctor had decided that playing the electric organ in the chapel might quiet me. As they grouped around me, Jerry and my cousins had all wondered, *Could she still play?* No one spoke or scarcely breathed. They said that for a long moment I sat, head bowed over the keyboard. Then, curving my fingers slightly, I lifted my hands from my lap. Trembling, I touched a note — then another — slowly sounding a few more tones and swelling it into full harmony. As the sweet music filled the room, the impact of the unsung words had hit them all —

> *"Count your blessings —*
> *Name them one by one"*

The family knew the time was approaching when I'd remember the heinous deeds or have to be told. It broke their hearts to lie to me and became increasingly difficult to find answers for my barrage of questions.

Although my recovery thus far had been miraculous, going home to my sisters in Potosi was impossible. But because of my restless questioning, the doctor knew the time had come for me to be told the truth. He said I must be in the home of some relative when this was done so that I would have at least some semblance of home. Thus, he released me to go to Gereldene's home — she lived closest of all the relatives —

before I really was strong enough physically or alert mentally.

When the moment of revelation had finally arrived here in Gereldene's home, they had prayed for strength and words from the only Source of light in the whole sordid story, for the neurologist had warned them of the possible consequences he feared. I could either grasp the truth — as I had done — and continue progressing toward recovery, or I could snap back into the shock tremors. Naturally, this was a traumatic experience for my loved ones as they faced the possible results of my learning the truth.

After another week I began hinting about when I could go home. At times it seemed like a place not far away, but at other times I thought *home* was nonexistent. Anyway, I wanted to see mother.

The doctors were pleased with my progress and agreed I could travel to Potosi. Mother was to be released from the Bonne Terre hospital and would go to Rosemary and Lee's home the day before I arrived.

The long ride to Potosi was further than I'd ever realized, and I was feverish from the alternating currents of expectation. One minute I felt the excitement of going home, and the next I was drenched with apprehension. *Home? How would mom look?* The folks had prepared me for her appearance; they said she had changed drastically from the ordeal.

For all the forewarning I'd had, I was still unprepared for what I saw. The weak and frail figure mother had been reduced to was beyond anything I had imagined. I hugged her, and we clung to each other. It had been so long. *How long?* There was still that sensation of timelessness.

Mother couldn't talk above a whisper, but her deep sigh was heartrending. It contained the essence of our smashed and battered lives.

Neither of us asked the questions crowding to the surface. For me, the crime was unfinished. This was a time of searching — desperately trying to comprehend my cul-de-sac. Every nerve was taut, and I felt the world was caving in; I was on unfamiliar ground.

Mother's face was gaunt. Her gray hair had been cropped for the extraction of a few of the myriad shot and metal chips under her scalp. Those scissions had left such angry-red, slow-healing wounds that the medical group attending her had decided to leave the rest of the scattered fragments in unless they found it necessary to remove them later. Her right arm was in a sling because of the mangled shoulder and broken collarbone. Too weak to use the fingers free of bandaging on her left hand, she required complete care.

Never was there a lack of sympathetic hands to minister to her needs, for devoted friends stayed with her and brought every imaginable gift and tantalizing food. Neighbors from Cub Creek, as well as those nearby and from town, were regular visitors, offering help and tending the farm and its produce. In a sense, their kind deeds were designed to offset the acts of swift destruction that had ravaged our family from the friendly community. A wedge of love was applied to mother's gaping loss, and even their presence served as a tonic aiding her recovery.

If home seemed far away or forever gone to mother and me, the place Rosemary and Lee made for us in their lives was a warmth that enfolded us like none we'd experienced.

The young couple's acceptance of a widow and a teen-ager and their concern for restoring our health prompted curative measures more beneficial than medical knowledge.

Lee was so disturbed about my vision that he brought cases of carrot juice and vegetable cocktail. I drank it and rested the long hours as I was supposed to while trying to get back to my normal self. Sometimes I refused to admit my weakness, my premature fatigue, and even my faulty eyesight.

One evening, in a mood of determination, I announced, "Nothing is wrong with me. I think I'll make some cookies." Yes, that was about as down-to-earth as anything I could think of. "Oatmeal cookies coming up!" I tried to imitate my old exuberance, but before I had even put the first ingredient in the mixing bowl, I felt the telltale weariness. But I wouldn't give up, and no one complained when the cookies weren't edible. I had misread the recipe. Instead of a half cup of sugar, I'd put in two cups. My head ached, and I went to bed.

Though the date wasn't certain, the family told me that the first of the murder trials would be coming up soon — perhaps in the fall. My testimony would be of great importance if my memory should return by then, so one afternoon in the late summer several law officers came to talk with me. They were gentle with their questioning, and I was fairly calm, although I had no answers yet.

"Do you remember the knock at your front door and going to answer it?"

"No."

"How about when you were in the kitchen and the boys told you to give them a drink?"

I shook my head, then closed my eyes and tried to picture the scene.

Mother spoke. "Do you remember standing there at the sink with a glass of water before he told us what to do?"

"No."

"And he started swearing — stomped his old hat —."

"Oh, *yes!*" Icy fingers gripped my heart as I recalled the fierce outburst. This was the horribly vivid nightmare I could never wake from. I was so badly shaken that the policemen stopped the questioning.

After this first breakthrough, details of the whole hideous experience filtered into my consciousness. They came gradually through the next days, but I was still caught between the dream world and reality.

Joe came with Jerry to see me a week after I'd come back to Potosi. That night I had the new and eerie sensation of trying to sort the past from the present. As the three of us sat on the front porch talking in the darkness, I almost asked why Bobbie hadn't come with Joe. I couldn't believe my friend was dead.

Another evening some girls came from Belgrade. I knew they were heartbroken about Bobbie, but they talked casually and lightheartedly with me because they didn't know whether I was ready to face her death yet.

After they'd gone I sat quietly with mother in the living room. Looking out the window into the darkness, I had the unreal impression — *Surely dad will be back. He must have gone to the city*. I knew the truth, but it was a fact I couldn't accept. Looking out into the deepest of nights, I also knew why I couldn't sleep near a window. What creatures lurked out there? *Someone with a gun?*

Murder In The Afternoon

The Farm . . .

In September I was able to
start school — that long-awaited senior year. My family and
I had discussed it carefully and had decided I would be
happier finishing with my old classmates in the Valley High
School. At first someone would drive me to and from school
until I was able to drive and meet the school bus at its first
stop halfway to Potosi. The school authorities assured me I
would have special permission to cut class periods short and
go to the lounge so I wouldn't become overtired.

I was thrilled with the arrangement and hoped to graduate
with my class. But that first day was not what I'd expected
of the first day of my glorious senior year. I was filled with
apprehension, still weak, tired easily, and the thought of
classrooms made my head ache. I wasn't the same happy-go-

lucky personality who had walked away from that school last May. Then life wore a face of sunlight, both around and in my spirit. The sun was still there, but it wore a different face. The light was too brilliant; it hurt my eyes and made me feel small and unprotected.

Most of all I dreaded that initial meeting with the kids. *How would they react to me? Would they think me some kind of freak? Did I look as different as I felt?* Though I wanted desperately to be myself, the lightheadedness gave me an ethereal feeling as if I were returning from another world.

Not wanting to admit my qualms, even to myself, I soon found that my worry had been unnecessary. The first two who greeted me were good friends. Their cheerful manner put me at ease, and soon I was absorbed in conversation. My friends came from every direction, and if anything, kids were jollier than ever, bent on helping me forget the horrible summer happenings.

The teachers were understanding, too, telling me I must not stay in class until I was exhausted, convincing me I could make up any lost time.

September also marked my first return to the farm. The family was reluctant to let me go, but I knew it was something I must do. Jerry encouraged me with, "There must be a first time," and he went out with me on a day when my sisters and their families were all there working.

Relatives and friends had been spending as much time as

possible working to put things in order. A hallmark of our community was how quickly they united to help in time of stress. Thus, they'd rallied in the early days of mourning to do the gardening and vegetable processing. Even so, they were hardly able to keep up with the routine as dad would have.

To further aggravate the family hardship, a new problem arose. When the livestock were counted, several of the prize registered Herefords were missing. Since only dad knew the exact number he had owned, there was no way for us to know how many were gone. Neighbors watched for clues, but they could only assume that trucks had hauled the animals away during the night.

Mother wasn't able to make the trip home yet, but aware of the uncontrollable circumstances, she decided to dispose of everything except the house and land — a difficult decision for her. Thus, on this September day we were sorting and preparing for the sale of farm machinery, livestock, and some household items.

When Jerry and I drove up to the front gate, I took a deep breath and a long look. Everything seemed so barren and devoid of life in that late afternoon sun. As Jerry went to join the men, I walked alone through the front yard toward the house that was no longer home. The roses by the fence were drooping, and the swing on the front porch sat idle. Inside the cool living room the drapes were open, but no light could brighten the sorrowful furnishings. It was so quiet in the big room, with only occasional voices filtering in from outside.

Physically spent, I knew I should lie down and rest. *But not here.* Ultimately I was drawn to the only object that looked inviting and unchanged. Like a reunion with a much-loved friend was my touch on the old upright piano.

It felt the same after all this time, although I couldn't remember when I'd last played it.

I moved aimlessly through the dining room where the silence seemed even deeper. And then to the kitchen. The unbearable kitchen. As I hurried past the white range toward the back door, the black gash on the oven door seemed to reach for me. Outside the bullet-riddled screen door, I paused, breathless, and leaned against the house. I found no sympathy in the gentle, peaceful hills. The long shadows reached darkly across the upper fields toward the bridge. Even the setting sun was harsh and mocking.

Crimson, bronze, and golden leaves covered the ground on the Sunday that mother made her first trip home. Mother and I had settled with Rosemary and Lee for an indefinite period and were slowly recovering physically. How long it would take us to regain emotional ground was uncertain. But in the meantime, my sister and her husband were creating a pleasant atmosphere that enveloped us in its security.

After church that morning mother had suggested, "Shall we drive out home this afternoon?" It was the first time she'd mentioned going as she tried to face the changes she knew had taken place since the day she was carried away in Melvin Taylor's car.

"We'll need to pick up walnuts for Christmas cookies — I guess," her voice was vague, half-hearted, as though she wondered whether there could be the usual festivities.

The family encouraged her to go, and I agreed, although

somewhere within me a voice taunted, *Home?* Jerry was home from college that weekend and offered to drive. I was glad he was there, for he was becoming dearer to me each day, as well as being a strong, secure link to days I had left behind. I was adapting to a new way of life and found it difficult to identify with my remote past and everything that had happened before that Saturday afternoon which marked the transition to the present scene. It seemed that a giant page in my life had been turned while I was asleep.

I knew I looked like my old self again. A skilled dentist had removed the tooth sliver and replaced the missing front tooth with a perfect replica. I'd regained my coloring and much of my natural exuberance, and I was active in church and youth group in town, singing with some of the same kids I used to wonder about.

Mother was learning to manipulate her left hand with its stub of a thumb and to use her right arm. A bulky pad rounded her shoulder to its normal contour. She'd gained strength slowly, debilitated by the physical suffering and shock, but more than anything by her poignant memories of the one she'd lost.

When we drove into the yard that Sunday afternoon, Jerry unexpectedly pulled up into the lane and parked. There was no sign of life as we walked past the house. It had been emptied several weeks before on the sale day. Now the fields were occupied by cattle which belonged to the lease holder.

Surrounded by hillsides bright with color, we tramped up the lane past the bleak house. We couldn't bring our-selves to go inside, but hurried toward the wood lot and the walnut trees behind the barn. We talked, especially Jerry and I, as we passed the barn and walked through the hay stubble around it, but never once did we look back.

And that was the way we left the place after our short walk and nut gathering. We drove up the road and across the bridge without turning to look at the house — afraid to look, for it seemed that dad would be standing there at the gate waving as he'd done every time someone left home.

Murder In The Afternoon

The Trials . . .

Thanksgiving season was near when the dreaded news came. Hank Jones's first trial had been set on the court docket. There had been a change of venue, and the trial was to be in Jefferson County. This trial would be for the murder of my father and would be followed by trials for the other three charges — the murder of Bobbie Lou and the attempted murders of mother and me.

Mother and I did not have to testify in any of Jones's trials, for he had pleaded guilty. Although we were relieved that we were not to be subpoenaed, we knew that eventually we would be for the trials of Jim Banks, who was to be tried in open court as an adult.

Trying to postpone the hideous ordeal I knew awaited us, I worked at pushing the memories from my mind. Soon enough I would have to delve into the buried past and recall every detail as if it were happening again. I knew this would require more emotional stamina than anything I had experienced since that bloody day.

Christmas came and its appropriate celebration, although this was the first time we had ever been away from the old farmhouse for that happy occasion. Vestiges of past holidays were with us — remembering dad and how he used to enjoy the early morning breakfast and then all those packages. He'd been the liveliest, bending under the tree as quick as any of the children. These were the good memories that were replacing the bad.

Mother, that spirited and efficient woman, was slipping back into her role as homemaker alongside her oldest daughter. As the winter progressed, she and Rosemary often entertained a houseful of friends and served delectable doughnuts and caramel-coated cinnamon rolls with coffee.

Mother gave occasional hints about going "back home." These weren't responded to, for she was still far from well physically, although she was rid of her sling and bandages.

She had gotten a job as a saleswoman in one of Potosi's department stores, and with persistence was making a new life for herself. Most of the suggestions she received were, "Buy a little house in town," but she did not take these hints.

Innumerable times strangers met this courageous woman in her new occupation and told how they had prayed for her. They admired her grit and her survival without bitterness or self-pity. But it was her tremendous faith in God that most impressed those who knew her and those who only knew about her.

One day Lee brought a traveling salesman to meet her.

"I just wanted to meet you," he smiled shyly. "I gave one of those pints of blood you needed last summer."

She said, "Thank you," although words always failed to express her deep gratitude.

I knew that feeling, too. At a mid-winter basketball game at school a young man approached me and explained that he had been the ambulance driver who had rushed me to the hospital. He then introduced a kindly gray-haired gentleman who was the physician in charge of the emergency station that was instrumental in saving my life.

In such unexpected meetings there was a depth of fervor not usually expressed between strangers. Mother and I were both experiencing the warm glow from all these people who had gone out of their way to show concern for our welfare and to say they were inspired by the Christian example of a family who had lived through such bloody torture.

Abruptly this warm glow was shattered by the long-dreaded appointment. The subpoenas were delivered, and mother and I were called as witnesses in the first trial of Jim Banks. He was to be tried for his part in dad's murder in St. Francois County shortly after Easter.

We were nearly sick with dread. Not only did we face the trial, but the realization that we would for the first time since that day in the kitchen come face-to-face with both Banks

and Jones, who was to testify at his accomplice's trial.
Mother was resolute and didn't allow herself to complain.
I barely mentioned my old fears, but the morning of the trial
I realized what a traumatic experience this was to be. Reliving
the day when bloodshed and death were all around. Those
horrible memories flooding back, to be repeated and
questioned. For I had finally regained every sketch of my
jagged memory. Right up to the last awful moment when
I'd breathed halting prayers, "Oh — Lord — help! This can't
be real!" Right up to the moment when that first blow fell!

Though we went to the trial with trepidation and testified
under great stress, we were able to leave early. The jury
reached a quick verdict. After the charge was reduced from
first to second degree murder, Banks was sentenced to ten
years in the penitentiary.

Out of this trial was to come one memory that remained
to haunt me and cause me to dread the others even more.
While I was waiting in the outer chamber (they called each
witness separately when it was time to testify), I happened
to lean forward and glance down the dusky corridor opposite
the closed door where we would be summoned.

The door to that inner chamber was closed, but its glass
panel gave me a clear view. There, surrounded by plain-
clothesmen, sat the older convict, Hank Jones. I was like a
child who cries over a ghoulish story yet asks to hear it
repeated. I couldn't restrain myself from looking down that
hallway again.

Evidently, from his arrogant attitude, he was enjoying
prison life as much as he'd expected. While he was still in
the county jail he'd been known to brag to his cronies outside the cell bars, "Goin' to my new home — at the Big
House!"

He was wearing a dark summer suit and white shirt, attire

that was the greatest contrast to the faded shirt and tight jeans he'd worn the day of the massacre. Not only were his clothes strikingly different today, but his whole profile was filled out.

He was laughing uproariously at some joke and seemed perfectly at ease among the dignified gentlemen. Could this debonair young man be the same hollow-cheeked killer I'd met at the front door that late afternoon last summer?

Then, as he leaned back laughing, I saw those teeth, and it was as if he were once more pushing me aside as he entered the door his partner opened!

Hank Jones had received two life sentences — one for each murder — and two seventy-five-year-sentences — one for each attempted murder — to be served consecutively. He did not appear at Banks' other trials.

Many changes occurred in my life during those months that marked space between the series of trials for the other charges against Banks. I had realized my deep love for Jerry Sadler, and he convinced me that I could finish college or music study after we were married. So on Valentine's Day, 1960, we became engaged.

There was the excitement of high school graduation and the honor of being one of the valedictory speakers, which was the glorious touch on the day that for a while had seemed an impossibility.

Through June and July there was the flurry of beginning courses at Flat River Junior College and the completing of plans for our August wedding. Ghosts of the past were easier to forget in the maze of college courses, music, new friends, and the anticipated wedding day.

Studies that interested me most were those which would later prove invaluable. In speech class I had to win the difficult battle to regain my self-confidence. It was to stand me in good stead, for the pressure of speaking before a jury of my peers made the difference in how I'd address large groups of adults later in my life.

English composition was a class that captivated me. The lively professor was one of a kind, a character with grizzled hair, twinkling blue eyes, and a droll smile set in a round face.

I found the elements of expression fascinating. In the creative sense it was almost second nature to me, so I enjoyed working at it. Taking words separately or in sentence structure and placing them in order to design a picture was like combining musical tones into pleasant harmony and leading through smooth chord progression in the many arrangements I'd done.

Near the end of the semester, the teacher asked for an essay on a subject depicting strong emotion. During that same week I was asked to lead an impromptu discussion in the youth group at church. Standing before the group, I surprised myself as much as anyone when I asked, "Ever wonder why you're still around? Alive?"

In carefree response they buzzed about it, never realizing that the essence of the question had been directed at myself. And I did not answer it until I'd begun that final writing assignment. Unveiling the traumatic struggle of my last year, I wrote expressing deep feeling. The typewritten pages I turned in rated me a top grade, and the professor's written comment was "Sincere and moving." But it meant more than that to me. It was to chart my course for life, for I had answered that question for myself: *Alive! God must have another purpose for me.*

Then the next ironic blow struck! In my hand was another official summons, an ugly reminder of the courtroom. The trial I dreaded more than any other — Bank's trial for Bobbie's murder — was scheduled for *two days after our wedding day!*

Jerry was with me when the subpoena came, and he was the calm support I needed. "We won't worry about it," he assured. "This time I can be with you."

Engrossed in the last round of summer activities, the final fittings of the wedding dress and going away outfit along with class assignments and finals, I managed to push thoughts of the gruesome trial aside most of the time.

Our wedding day was a beautiful oasis in that year of torment. My oldest brother-in-law, Lee, gave me away, and Jerry and I said our vows in the presence of dear friends and family. Everything was perfect — the ceremony, the reception with the beautiful decorations and the unbelievably long row of tables loaded with gifts. I couldn't believe it was all happening and could not refrain from repeating, "I just don't deserve all this."

I had shoved the grim memory shadows into the furthest recesses of my being and barred the door against them. Temporarily, they would stay locked away. I had no way of knowing that they would one day force their way to the forefront in my life, that the full impact I'd never been able to face squarely would have to be dealt with eventually — in God's time.

Wearing a powder blue dress from my trousseau, I walked to the witness stand two days after my wedding day and for the second time reentered the mental dungeon to describe the killers' acts.

I was nauseated from the tension and the methodical, droning procedure in the courtroom. When my turn came to testify and I was called in from the outer chamber, I took the oath, walked up the three steps to a chair the state's attorney indicated, and sat down, perfectly erect. A measure of courage was returning, but I still wasn't sure about the tough decision I had to make. The lawyer had talked to me about it, leaving it to my discretion.

Should I even consider it? I had wondered since the matter first came up during the counsel mother and I had had with the prosecutor the week before. The mild-mannered attorney explained why our testimonies were so vital in this case. He'd stressed that each offense was tried separately and only evidence pertinent to that individual act would be accepted. This jury wouldn't consider the murder at the store minutes before Bobbie's. At the spring trial for dad's murder, Banks had definitely been shown to have been implicated. There was his signed confession that he'd helped Jones plan the crime and had fulfilled his role by ordering the bologna sandwich to distract the unsuspecting grocer's attention. Also, there was the farmer down the creek who had testified that he saw Banks carrying the gun as he and Jones walked up the road past his house.

In this trial, then, the emphasis must be on the eyewitness accounts of all that had happened in the kitchen. The lawyer had gone over every detail with mother and me in advance. When we came to the boys' behavior and vulgar threats, I was wide-eyed, fearful.

"Repeat those *filthy words?*"

"It's up to you," the lawyer said sympathetically. "But it might help the jury get the picture — by repeating their crude words and speech."

Of course I knew mother could never say those words. *And neither can I!* Then I thought, *Should I try? For this reason? Would it really make a difference in the final verdict?*

Now the select jurors were in place and had been shown pieces of evidence, Banks' signed confession and the broken shotgun. Later I learned that there were one or two pictures, too. I wasn't in the courtroom when mother testified, of course, but she told me that when she was shown an enlargement of her kitchen and asked to identify it, she broke down and cried uncontrollably.

My turn had finally come. The state's attorney stood facing me. He spoke kindly, wording the questions carefully. In spite of this, I felt shrouded by the ugly scene. The walls were pressing in on me.

Once I looked around and noted a familiar face in the visitors' section near the back of the courtroom. The man who sat staring at the judge was Bobbie's father. He looked miserable, as if he couldn't bear another word, yet was unable to pull himself from the court session.

The lawyer was asking the questions that I expected, mostly repetitions from the last trial. He asked for a description of the older killer, then his partner.

"Is he in this room?"

"Yes, sir."

"Will you point him out?"

I looked toward Banks who sat midway down the long dark table with his defender. The young criminal raised his head briefly as I lifted a trembling hand to single him out. His wary glances darted to me, the jury at the front end of his table, and around the room. Then he lowered his head and continued to stare at the wooden surface, his eyes only inches above the table top. He swiped the oily strings of hair from his eyes, and his expression was guarded, like a stealthy animal watching for traps.

Asked to give the full story of what had happened, I plunged into the all-too-vivid memory. I was terrified, haunted by those last awful moments of staring into the cold steel gun barrel. Forcing myself on from one word to another brought the whole nightmare pounding down on me.

As he'd promised, the prosecutor worded the worst question so that I could answer with a general statement or repeat words verbatim. His voice was even; he might have been asking about my homemaking skills.

"Did they make any demands of you?"

There was no more time for me to weigh my decision. *Should I? Or not?* Well aware of the cunning frame-up the defense was posing to free the younger assailant of further charges, I looked at the jurors. Their expressions were solemn. I couldn't tell how they were accepting the story. Would this shocking discourse make the difference?

I spit out the words with disgust as though they were refuse to be expelled as quickly as possible. Immediately I wished I hadn't. From that moment, every thought of it caused me to grind my teeth.

Weak and nauseated, I managed to finish the hideous story, and then it was time for the defense to cross-examine. I was quaking inside as I watched the stocky lawyer stand up next to his young client.

This was the glib advocate the Banks family had hired, and he was, by his own definition, champion-of-justice. His black hair was slicked like satin from a right side part. Across his eyes and forehead was a youngish look, but this was belied by his stodgy build. With a flourish, he brushed each of his sleeves and then the coattail of his shiny blue suit. He addressed me with a patronizing smile.

"Mrs. Ella Jo Barr Sadler." Pursing his lips, he stood looking at me while the courtroom waited without a sound. Then he folded his arms. "Who carried the gun into the kitchen?"

That was all. After a couple more questions, I was dismissed to sit with Jerry among the spectators.

Young Bonnie Sue Midgett was among the twenty other witnesses. She'd seen the living and dead victims just before and after the crime, sights which would haunt for a lifetime. The depth of blood in the kitchen that afternoon was a sickening picture she was totally unprepared to face. When they'd arrived at the same house where she'd just taken her piano lesson, mother's brother, John Hutchings, was coming out the front door. On his face was a crazed expression, and his words were barely intelligible, "Help! Maybe dead!"

The gray-haired man then led them to the kitchen where he'd happened on the unexpected red pool a few minutes earlier when he'd come to the store and found the door closed but saw other neighbors going into the house. Feverishly they'd worked, pulling towels from every drawer and closet in the futile effort to swab our punctured heads.

But there was no opportunity at the trial for Bonnie Sue to describe this bloody scene. Like all the other witnesses, there were so many things she would have told the jury, but the attorney had cautioned her against using more words than the specific questions called for. He knew the defense would be quick with objections any time a flaw could be picked in a statement, or as he'd term it, "Facts not pertinent to the case."

Bonnie Sue was pale and shaken when she came to sit by me, and we strengthened each other as we sat through the remainder of the state's witnesses and then the witnesses called by the defense.

No match for the first eloquent speaker, the defender made a short speech. His method was a play on sympathy. First it was the "head in the clouds" theory. He'd have the jury remember that this kid shared eight bottles of beer a short five hours and a twelve-mile-walk before the killings. Then there was the "mother and home" appeal.

"This little boy wants to get home to help with gardening. He loves it. Why, every day after school. . . ." On he went, gesticulating with wide arm motions.

It was real agony to hear this discourse at each trial, especially when the pain and loss were so fresh and acute.

Late that Monday afternoon the jury entered their private room for deliberation. As soon as the judge informed the people that a verdict probably would not be reached for several hours, possibly not until the next day, everyone left the courthouse.

Weary and depressed, Jerry and I spent the night in Potosi. We hoped to hear the outcome of the trial early in the morning and then be on our way on our postponed honeymoon.

The jury was detained overnight. It wasn't until Tuesday afternoon that the members were dismissed, failing to reach a verdict. The judge declared it a mistrial!

Murder In The Afternoon

Return to Life . . .

The time spent on the witness stand was only a tiny portion of what that trial actually cost in emotional strain. But now that that worst was over, I was determined to return to a normal life.

After a wonderful honeymoon, we returned to our apartment near the city, and all those lovely wedding gifts were unpacked and placed in our first home.

As Jerry resumed his work, I was busy with my music and auditions. I got a part-time job at a music studio, began taking additional lessons on the organ, and at the midwinter semester started back to college.

But near the end of the school year, certain danger signals began appearing. Years later I was to view this period of my life in relation to something the Lord said to Peter: "Satan desired to sift you as wheat."

Within a few months, two more trials came and went. Banks was given a ten-year sentence at each of these, making a total of thirty years for him to serve. However, the gruesome ordeal never got any easier for me. Each time it took longer to pull out of those vivid memories and run from them again.

This was just the beginning of the horrible nightmares I woke from many nights. To turn on a light and know they weren't true was a relief, but to erase the feeling would take more than a day each time. The nameless dread wasn't to be driven away.

Aggravated by the rising crime rate, the double-faced specter reared from my memory closet, and an awareness of it became more intense with every newspaper story I read of murder, and particularly "mad-dog attacks."

Sometimes when I was shopping or browsing leisurely at the library, I'd glimpse a peculiar feature in a stranger. Maybe it would be a mannerism like a twitching of bony shoulders, or a slouched kid whose greasy, stringy hair was falling in his eyes, or a toothy grin. Suddenly, in a tremor of the old shock, I'd expect to see a gun raised toward me, and I'd run to the car and drive home. Not until I was safely past the experience would I chide myself — *Imagination! Probably. A gun? In broad daylight?* It happens sometimes, I was forced to admit.

There was an old chant from inside my locked memory, *Oh, Lord! This can't be real!* Severe chest pains that followed these bouts with agonizing fear were convincing me of the truth I was trying to ignore.

Anxious wondering led me into startling traps. I still couldn't think of dad and Bobbie as being dead, though I pondered the thoughts until death, itself, finally became a reality. That was the clincher that robbed me of security. *Who'll be next? Murdered?* I thought about my husband. *He's too young!* The menacing echoes rang down the corridors of my mind. *Too young?* Young? Young? *Young?*

Some nights I woke trembling, "Where is everyone? They're all gone — I'm alone!" When the light was turned on I'd recover, and Jerry would be there, his caress tender yet strong, to shatter the gloom.

"It's okay, honey. I'm here," he'd say gently. Then I could go back to sleep.

Most disturbing of the changes I was undergoing was what happened to my music performance. The drive was still there to fulfill the deep desire I'd had from childhood, but something in the emotional upheaval struck a blow to my self-confidence.

I was getting hours of practice every day on my difficult assignments. I played in programs with professional musicians, and once did, from memory, a thirty-one-page contemporary composition. Yet, I sensed a loss of control. With all the drills I worked at daily, my technique seemed unimproved. Every thought of insecurity that taunted me made future goals less certain.

If there was anything sure about my skill, it was the fact that I'd believed all my life and often repeated to myself, "If God gives a talent, He'll help you multiply it and use it for His glory."

I hadn't lost faith in God or stopped serving Him even though I was under great stress. I still accompanied church services regularly, and felt the Lord was developing and using my talent even when I was being tested and almost defeated by Satan.

Besides the focus on this well-defined purpose I'd always possessed, I could think of other reasons to battle the doubts.

Quitting was never a consideration in my home. *Mother and dad would be so disappointed if I ... but dad. . . .* There it was again, and I still couldn't face it. My mind refused to tell me where he'd gone, but I often caught myself assuming he'd be back sometime.

The nearest I'd come to tears was one fall afternoon in the cemetery. Standing there at the grave side, I'd read the tombstone inscription. Down the hill and across the road I could hear Cub Creek trickling a playful tune where the upper branch flowed into it. *Dad fished up that creek many times.* I gazed across the flat field beyond the peaceful stream. *He got a deer right over there one season — a huge buck.* I walked slowly back to the car, thinking, *He must be around here somewhere.* I felt sure he couldn't be in that spot marked with his name in stone.

B y the end of the semester, I was even more distressed — not satisfied with my accomplishment, but confused about the real root of my problem. I had a long talk with mother, who understood that I was tearing myself apart.

She came up for a visit, and the two of us sat at the tiny apartment-size table. Lacing her fingers around her coffee cup, mother suggested, "Maybe you should ease off for a year or so. Get a job — something entirely different. Keep up your private lessons, but I think you need a break from this struggle."

That was just the advice I needed. The idea was exciting — a change of pace — and that way I could afford the organ

I'd been wanting. So after a summer's training period on data-processing equipment, I got a position in the accounting department of a large bank. At the same time I kept up my piano and organ practice and my private lessons.

My job was interesting, and I was busy, especially when Jerry and I found a house and were considering how we could furnish it.

One afternoon I took trays of my key-punched cards to the collator, a machine which was located in an isolated corner. This task was routine — cards from two trays had to be placed in separate stackers so the machine could merge them in proper sequence — so while I worked there alone, my mind was occupied with arranging furniture in the new home.

Some of my parents' furniture had been put into storage for me to have when Jerry and I bought a home. As I thought about dad's chair and where I'd put it, I was gripped with a strange feeling — *I can't just carry off dad's favorite chair!*

Then, for the first time, the truth stabbed my consciousness. *But he won't need it any more!*

Suddenly the machine and punched cards blurred before my eyes as the tears flowed at the breakthrough of complete realization.

Time and healing instilled a new range of vision in mother and me, but not until each of us was thrust before a new frontier. Answers were slow in coming, directions not clear-cut, for none of our acquaintances had been over this path.

One weekend in late winter, two-and-a-half years after that July day, mother and I made a trip back to the farm. As we drove, we had much to talk about. Alike in disposition, we'd analyze situations and try to find something humorous about the toughest experiences. That day our talk centered in a new depth of our shared trauma.

Mother had had to overcome the tremors of having been swept off her own doorstep and her increasing desire to return. For me, the battle was with the phantom representative of the crime world.

"This old nagging fear trails me. It's one of the worst kinds of torture," I told her. I knew mother was not afraid, but though I could overcome the horror for long periods, it still lurked in my subconscious and I was, in effect, held prisoner by that dread of being attacked or held at gunpoint.

"But I keep reminding myself of the psalmist's promise from God, 'Mere earthly men will terrify no longer,' and I know someday it will be true for me."

Looking up from the steering wheel, mother announced abruptly, "Think I'll move back home when the lease is up this spring." She had dropped hints before, but nothing this definite. The farmland had been leased to one man, and another family was renting the house.

"Maybe I can get out there in time to plant a small garden." She spoke as though she'd decided already, but then she added, "What do you think?"

"Well, mom, if you're sure that's what you want. Are you sure you're ready? I mean to face the memories and —?"

"Memories, sure! It's home. That's why I want to go back."

We rode on in silence for a time before I asked, "The rest of the family's against it, aren't they?"

"You should hear them! 'Why on *earth* would Valle want to go out there? She should know she'll never make it — Lynn's gone — the children. And after all that *happened* there!' " She parroted. "Guess they all think I'm nuts."

"Have you considered your health?"

"That's another thing they poke at me, 'What about your throat, Valle? Maybe you're not as strong as you once were. The winters are so cold — and that old house.' They tell me I'll die of pneumonia or something else."

We both remembered past winters sleeping in unheated bedrooms. I particularly cringed at the thought of early days after mother's tracheostomy when respiratory problems and pneumonia occurred often and were a real threat to her life.

"Who knows? Maybe I'll install a central heat system." With a wry grin, she added, "Eventually." She seemed to desire my approval, but indicated that her mind was set anyway.

"Oh, I know it won't be easy, but if the Lord lets me live — you know I thought of something the other day. Wish I'd kept a list of how many evangelists, musicians, and Christian leaders we've entertained, that I've cooked for and served. Remember how they all prayed before leaving, 'Bless this home,' or words to that effect?"

"Yes."

"Well, when I think of all those prayers," mother said seriously, "maybe the Lord isn't through blessing our home!"

Murder In The Afternoon

Epilogue . . .

Under blue summer skies, the
peaceful countryside around the farming community of
Quaker, Missouri, is a landscape of patchwork design.
Ripening grain fields, in hues ranging from maize to shades
of deep gold, are interspersed with lush green pastures. The
fences enclosing various sections are lined with foliage, and
huge trees trace shallow branches of Cub Creek as it
meanders through the area.

The lives of the inhabitants of this isolated farming
region are as peaceful and ordinary as their setting. God-
fearing, respectable citizens for the most part, they spend
their days reaping the abundant harvests, enjoying
neighborly gatherings and church meetings, and leading
lives common to any farming community.

Little hills rise out of the meadows like bulges in a soft carpet, and occasionally a higher crest overlooks the lower expanses. The most prominent of these is a lofty peak that commands a view of the sprawling Barr valley and the secluded site of the Barr farm.

Sixteen years have passed since that July day claimed the life of my father and my friend. The giant maple trees still stand in the yard before the big white house, where they shelter many family gatherings, for mother lives there with her bachelor brother. She has carved out a new life for herself, earning her certificate as a nurses' assistant and working in a hospital and a senior citizen hospital care unit. The old home has so much left of the memories that nothing can scar — memories that have stood the test of time, like the family that gathers there.

And after all these years there has been a new beginning for me, Ella Jo. I have not always understood God's leading, but I have always tried to follow. At times I thought I'd beaten down the last of those shadowy creatures in my memory, but then they would rise out of the past to try and conquer me. I seldom talked about the crime, for remembering caused me to tremble. It was almost beyond my endurance to even drive or ride through the area where the prison is located.

But my greatest test and the privilege to overcome, at last, was so incredible that without divine guidance my story still might have ended tragically. For the paradox of my life is that I had to finish this book before my story was complete. And when I finally did begin writing it, I came to a crucial decision. I felt that I couldn't really display a victorious faith in God unless I could be honest with myself and God and determine whether I'd really forgiven those who had so deliberately snatched my loved ones. And it was at that point that I could say, "Jesus forgave His murderers on the spot. It's taken me eleven years!"

It was in coming to grips with the fear, in writing about the entire ordeal and facing the hidden memories, that I found the touchstone which released me from the fear I knew I could not live with indefinitely.

I've come such a long way, and I truthfully say I can trust the Lord, even at my weakest moment — answering an unexpected knock. I can trust the Lord — even after learning that the younger man is out on parole. Even after learning that following a series of appeals the oldest of the two is to have a retrial and once more mother and I may have to endure the gruesome ordeal of the courtroom.

It is as if our whole family is back to the starting place after the bloodshed which has been our crucible for testing. Now the story is written, but these pages, bloody though some may be, are only a small part in the account of faith's continued story.

> *"Disaster strikes like a cyclone and the*
> *wicked are whirled away, but the good*
> *man has a strong anchor."*